WYDANIE NARODOWE
DZIEŁ FRYDERYKA CHOPINA

NATIONAL EDITION
OF THE WORKS OF FRYDERYK CHOPIN

BALLADES
Opp. 23, 38, 47, 52

NATIONAL EDITION
Edited by JAN EKIER

The Foundation
for the National Edition
of the Works of Fryderyk Chopin

PWM
EDITION

SERIES A. WORKS PUBLISHED DURING CHOPIN'S LIFETIME. VOLUME I

FRYDERYK CHOPIN

BALLADY
op. 23, 38, 47, 52

WYDANIE NARODOWE
Redaktor naczelny: JAN EKIER

FUNDACJA WYDANIA NARODOWEGO
POLSKIE WYDAWNICTWO MUZYCZNE
KRAKÓW 2023

SERIA A. UTWORY WYDANE ZA ŻYCIA CHOPINA. TOM I

Redakcja tomu: Jan Ekier, Paweł Kamiński

Do każdego tomu dołączone są w formie luźnej wkładki *Komentarz wykonawczy*
i *Komentarz źródłowy (skrócony).*

Pełne *Komentarze źródłowe* do poszczególnych tomów będą publikowane oddzielnie.

Wydany w oddzielnym tomie *Wstęp do Wydania Narodowego Dzieł Fryderyka Chopina
1. Zagadnienia edytorskie* obejmuje całokształt ogólnych problemów wydawniczych,
zaś *Wstęp… 2. Zagadnienia wykonawcze* – całokształt ogólnych problemów interpretacyjnych.

Editors of this Volume: Jan Ekier, Paweł Kamiński

A *Performance Commentary* and *Source Commentary (abridged)*
are included in each volume in the form of a loose insert.

Full *Source Commentaries* on each volume will be published separately.

The *Introduction to the National Edition of the Works of Fryderyk Chopin
1. Editorial Issues*, published as a separate volume, covers general matters concerning the publication.
The *Introduction… 2. Performance Issues* covers all general questions of interpretation.

Ballada g-moll op. 23 / Ballade in G minor Op. 23   page / s. 11

Ballada F-dur op. 38 / Ballade in F major Op. 38   page / s. 26

Ballada As-dur op. 47 / Ballade in A♭ major Op. 47   page / s. 36

Ballada f-moll op. 52 / Ballade in F minor Op. 52   page / s. 48

about the Ballades...

Op. 23

"I received a new Ballade from Chopin. It seems to be a work closest to his genius (although not the most ingenious) and I told him that I like it best of all his compositions. After quite a lengthy silence he replied with emphasis, 'I am happy to hear this since I too like it most and hold it dearest'."

From a letter by Robert Schumann to Heinrich Dorn, Leipzig 14 September 1836.

Op. 38

"[...] send me [...] the manuscript of my last Ballade because I want to see something."

From a letter by F. Chopin to Julian Fontana in Paris, Nohant 8 August 1839.

"The passionate episodes seem to have been added later; I recall precisely, that while playing the Ballade [September 1836], Chopin ended it in F major; now it ends in A minor."

Robert Schumann *Gesammelte Schriften über Musik und Musiker*, Leipzig 1888, vol. III.

"Madame Viardot told me that Chopin frequently played the opening Andantino but never that what follows."

Camille Saint-Saëns *Etude des Variantes* in "Trois manuscrits de Chopin", Paris 1932.

Op. 47

"Tomorrow you shall receive the Nocturne, and by the end of the week the Ballade [...] I am unable to polish it sufficiently."

From a letter by F. Chopin to Julian Fontana in Paris, Nohant 18 October 1841.

Op. 52

"Dear Sirs. I would like to offer you a Scherzo (for 600 fr.), a Ballade (for 600 fr.), and a Polonaise (for 500 fr.) [...]. If you find my Scherzo, Ballade and Polonaise acceptable, please write by the nearest post, indicating the term by which you would wish me to send these compositions. Sincerely devoted Fr. Chopin."

From a letter by F. Chopin to the Breitkopf & Härtel firm in Leipzig, Paris 15 December 1842.

o Balladach...

Op. 23

„Od Chopina dostałem nową Balladę. Wydaje mi się być najbliższym jego geniuszu
(nie najgenialniejszym) dziełem i powiedziałem mu, że ze wszystkich jego dzieł najbardziej ją lubię.
Po dłuższym namyśle odparł mi z naciskiem: «To mnie cieszy, bo i ja najwięcej ją lubię,
jest mi najdroższa»."

Z listu Roberta Schumanna do Henryka Dorna, Lipsk 14 IX 1836.

Op. 38

„[...] przyślij mi [...] moją ostatnią Balladę w manuskrypcie, bo chcę coś widzieć."

Z listu F. Chopina do Juliana Fontany w Paryżu, Nohant 8 VIII 1839.

„Pełne namiętności części łącznikowe wydają się być dodane później; przypominam sobie dokładnie,
że Chopin grając tutaj [IX 1836] Balladę kończył ją w F-dur; obecnie kończy się ona w a-moll."

Robert Schumann *Gesammelte Schriften über Musik und Musiker*, Lipsk 1888, tom III.

„Pani Viardot mówiła mi, że Chopin często grał jej początkowe Andantino, nigdy jednak nie grał tego,
co po nim następuje."

Camille Saint-Saëns *Etude des Variantes* w „Trois manuscrits de Chopin", Paryż 1932.

Op. 47

„Jutro dostaniesz Nokturna, a ku końcu tygodnia Balladę [...] nie mogę dosyć wykończyć."

Z listu F. Chopina do Juliana Fontany w Paryżu, Nohant 18 X 1841.

Op. 52

„Szanowni Panowie. Mam do zaofiarowania Panom Scherzo (za 600 fr.), Balladę (za 600 fr.),
Poloneza (za 500 fr.) [...]. Jeżeli moje Scherzo, Ballada i Polonez odpowiadają Panom, proszę mi
napisać słówko najbliższą pocztą, wskazując termin, w którym by Panowie sobie życzyli, abym te
utwory wysłał.
          Szczerze oddany Fr. Chopin"

Z listu F. Chopina do firmy Breitkopf & Härtel w Lipsku, Paryż 15 XII 1842.

Ballade   *A Monsieur le Baron de Stockhausen*

op. 23

Largo*

Moderato

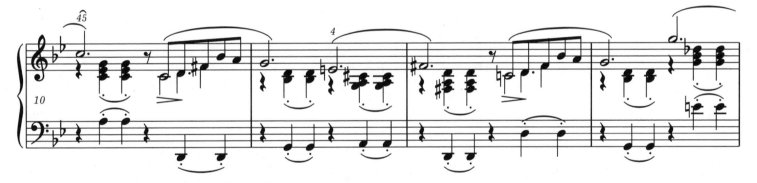

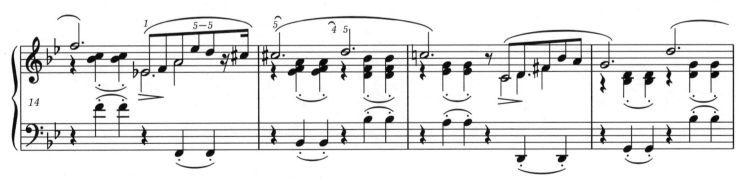

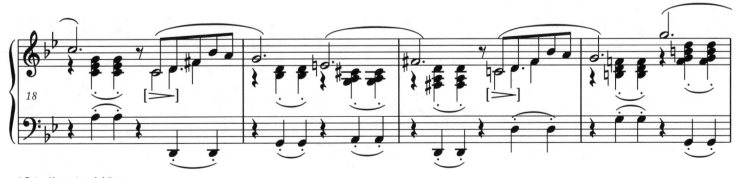

* Patrz *Komentarz źródłowy.*
  Vide Source Commentary.

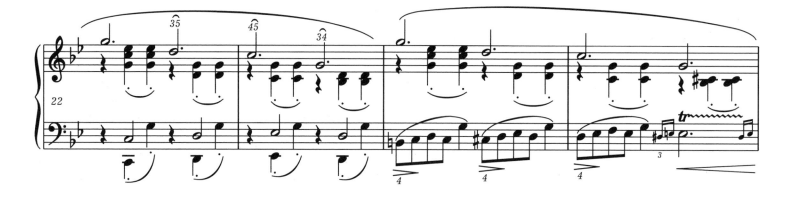

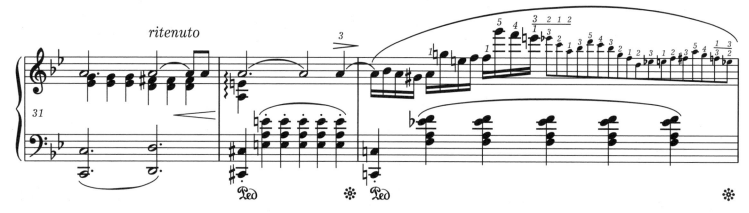

PWM-4927

sempre più mosso

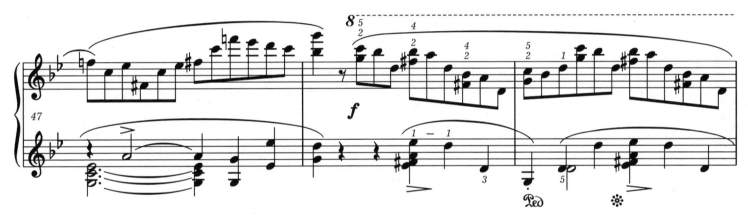

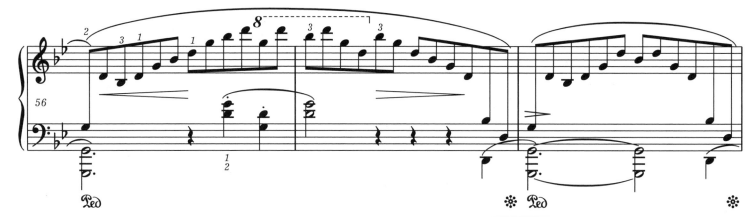

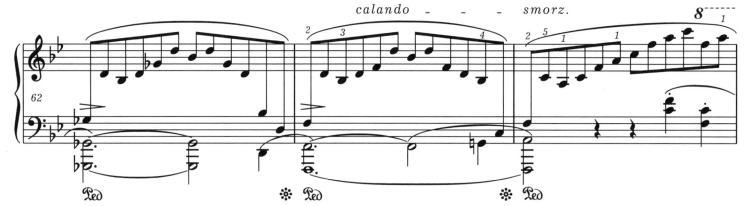

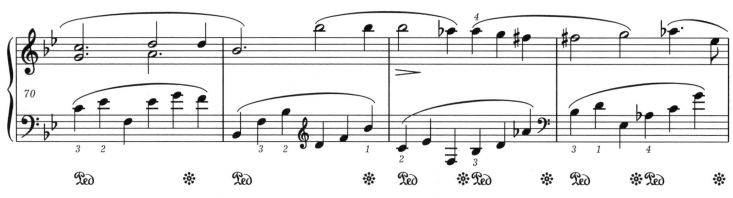

PWM-4927

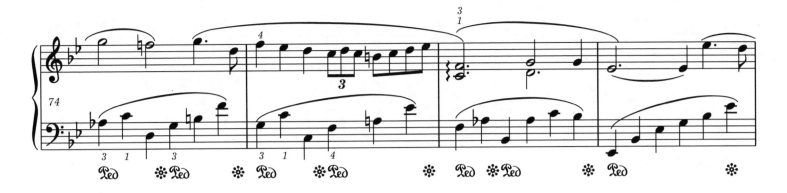

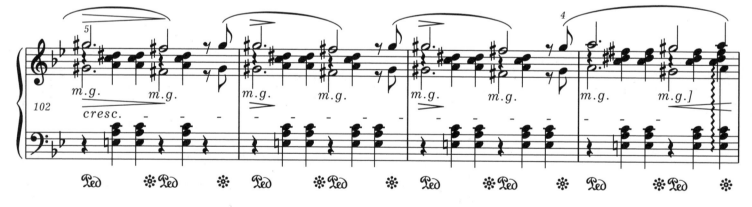

PWM-4927

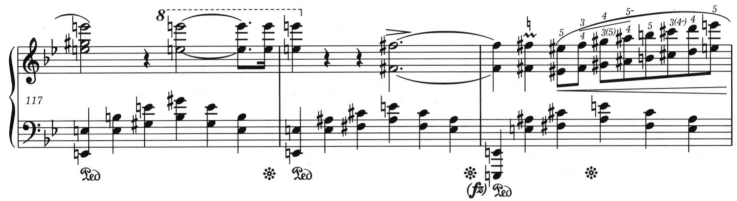

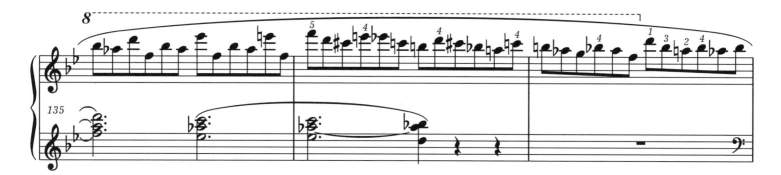

PWM-4927

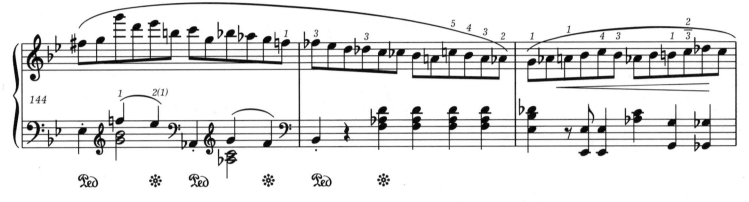

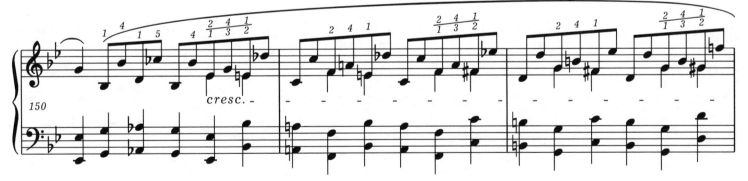

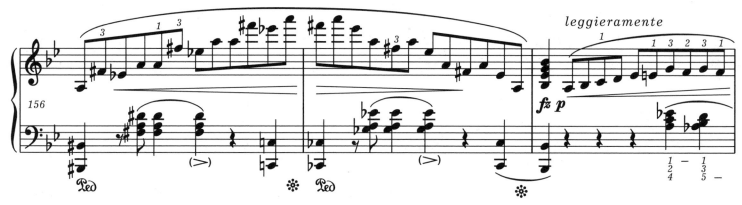

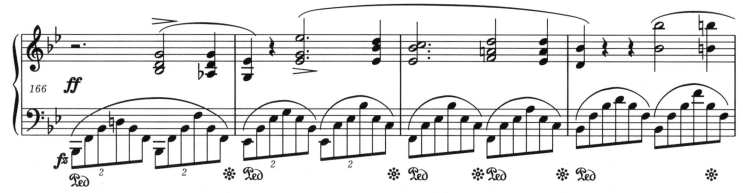

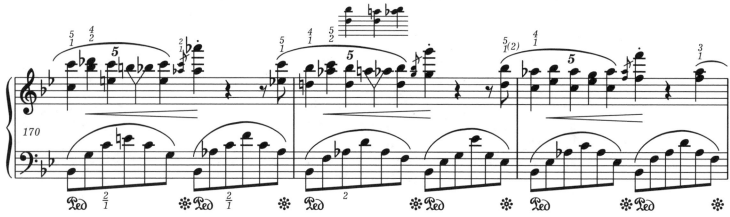

PWM-4927

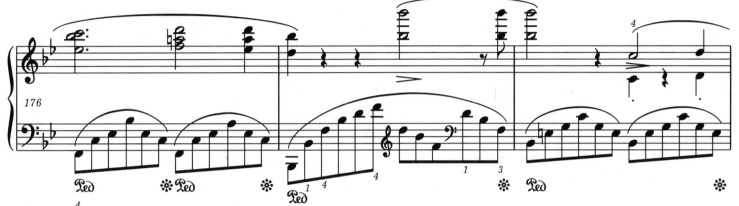

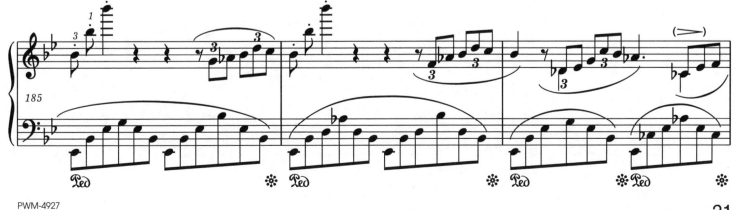

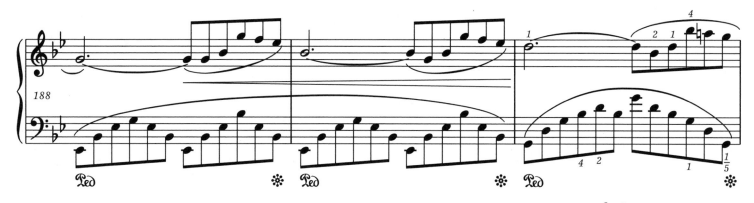

PWM-4927

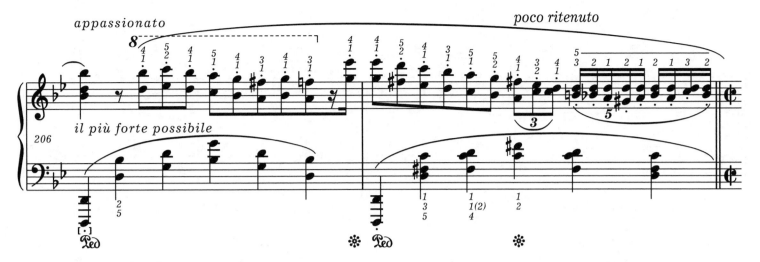

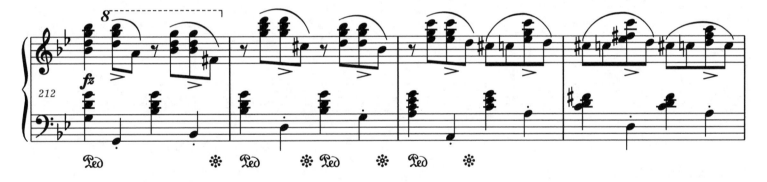

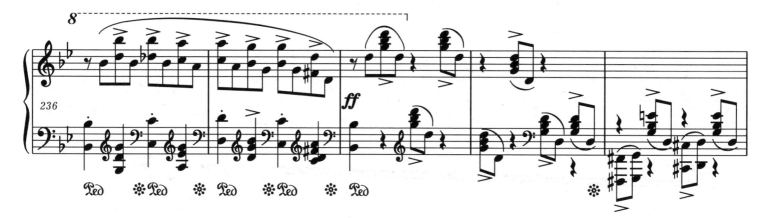

PWM-4927

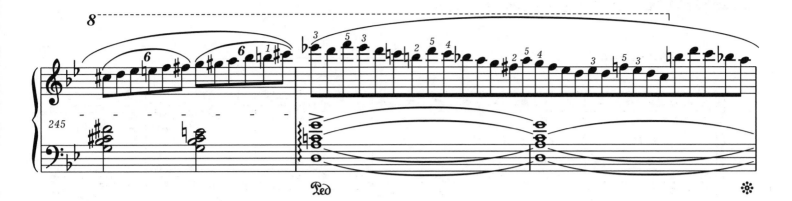

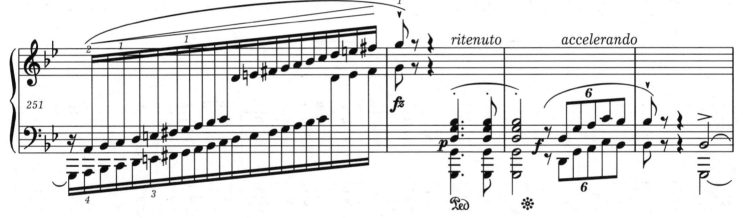

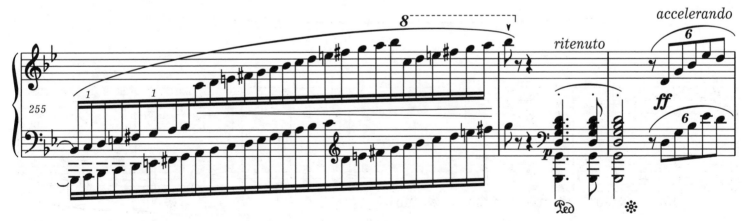

PWM-4927

Ballade
A Monsieur Robert Schumann

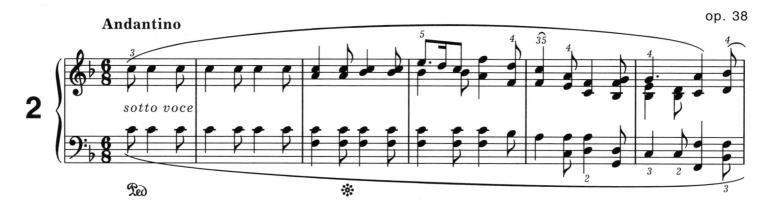

PWM-4927

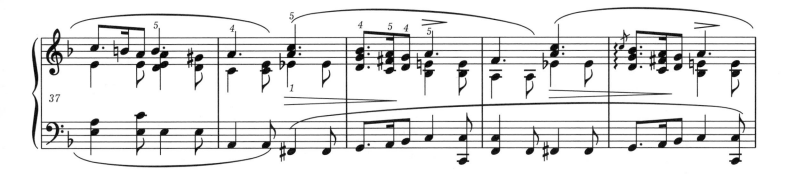

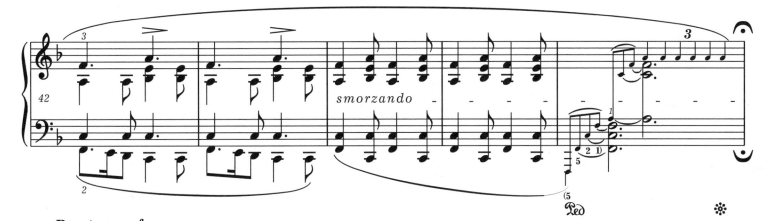

Presto con fuoco

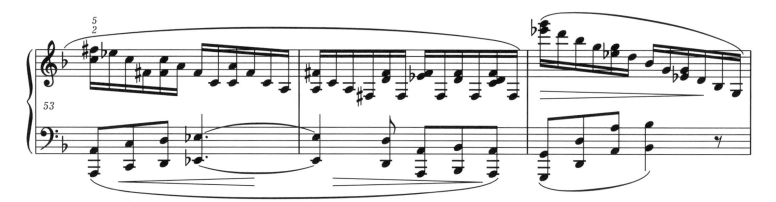

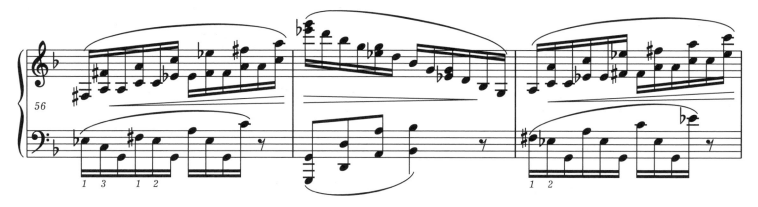

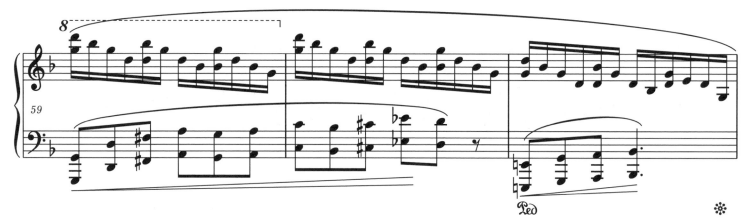

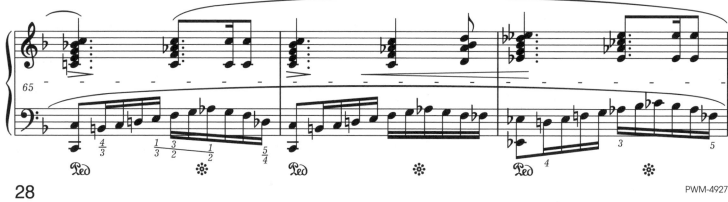

PWM-4927

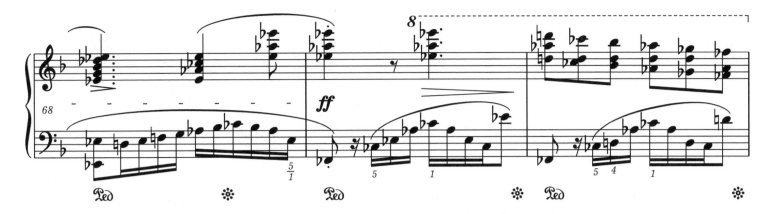

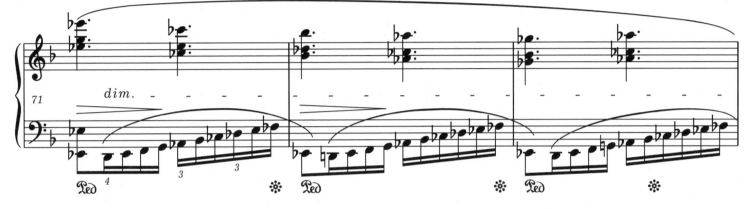

* Górne dźwięki oktaw należy również powtórzyć.
  The upper notes of the octaves must also be repeated.

30

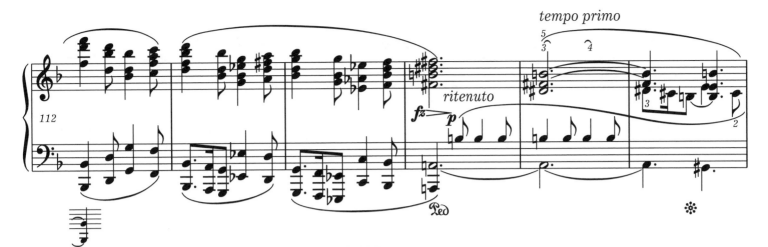

Presto con fuoco

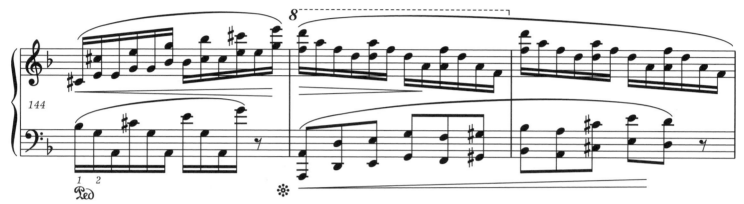

PWM-4927

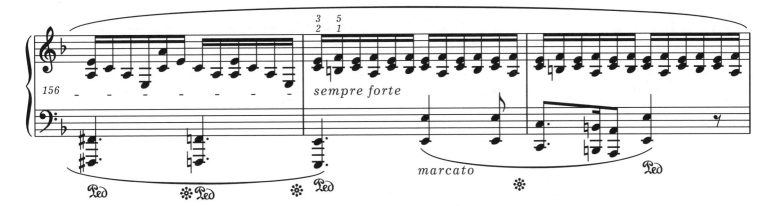

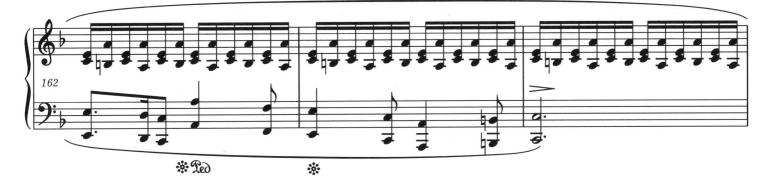

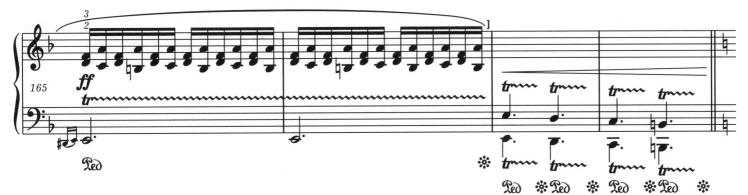

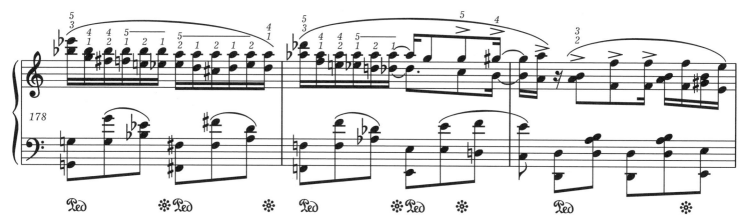

PWM-4927

Ballade

A Mademoiselle Pauline de Noailles

op. 47

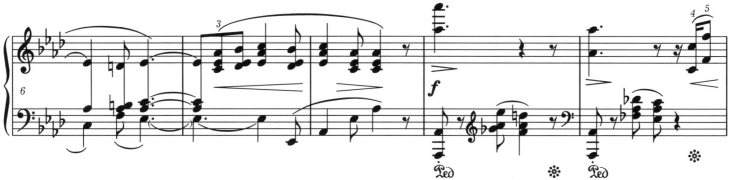

* Dźwięk *as* należy powtórzyć.   * The note *ab* should be repeated.

PWM-4927

* **tr** = ⁓

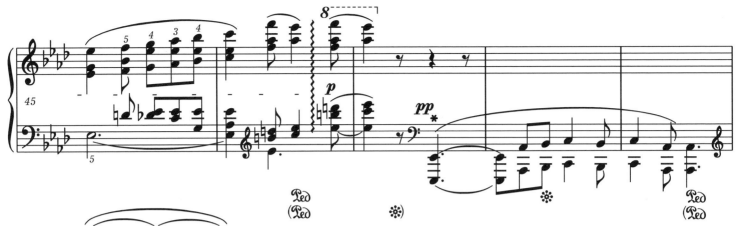

*ossia:

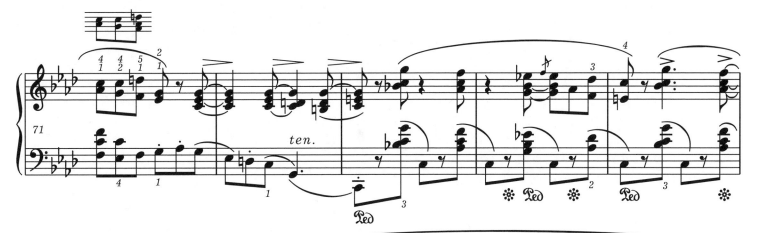

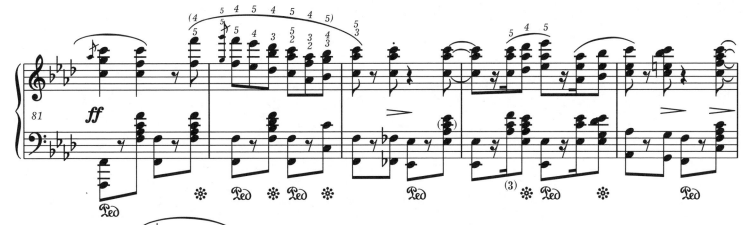

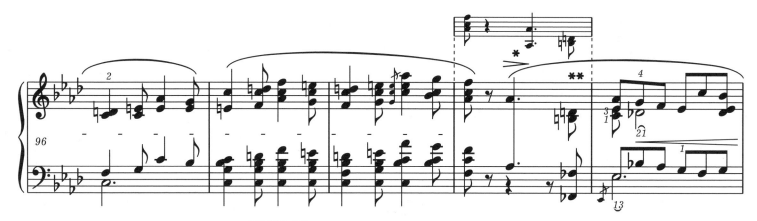

* Tekst główny i wariant podają dwa sposoby odczytania niejasnego w źródłach zapisu rytmicznego tego taktu. Patrz *Komentarz źródłowy.*
  The main text and the variant contain two ways of reading the rhythmic record of the text, unclear in the sources. *Vide Source Commentary.*

** *ossia:* t. 99-100: ♪♪ lub ♪♪ t. 101-102: ♪♪
   bars 99-100: or bars 101-102:

Nie należy stosować tych wariantów w obu miejscach naraz. Patrz *Komentarz źródłowy.*
These variants should not be used simultaneously. *Vide Source Commentary.*

*** W jednym z egzemplarzy lekcyjnych Chopin objął łukiem frazę utworzoną przez akcentowane najwyższe dźwięki l.r. w t. 109-112.
    In one of the pupils' copies, Chopin slurred a phrase created by the accented L.H. top notes in bars 109-112.

**** Dźwięk *as'* należy powtórzyć.
     The note *ab'* should be repeated.

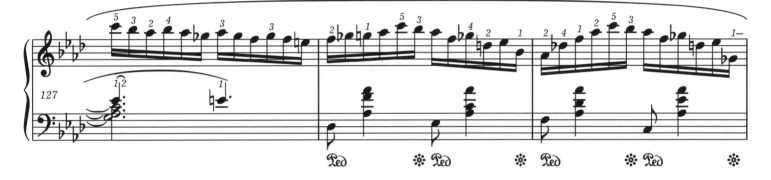

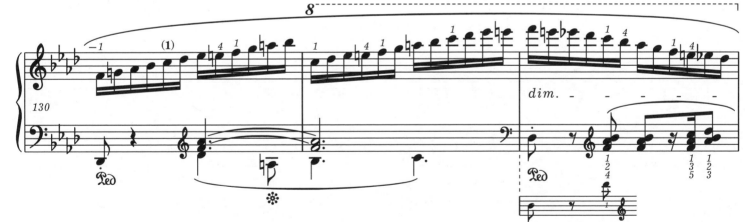

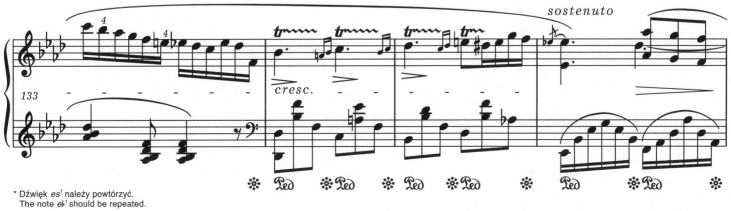

* Dźwięk *es¹* należy powtórzyć.
  The note *eb¹* should be repeated.

41

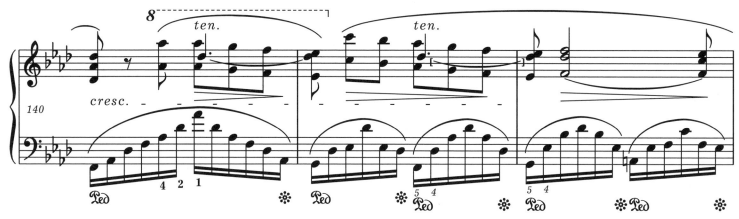

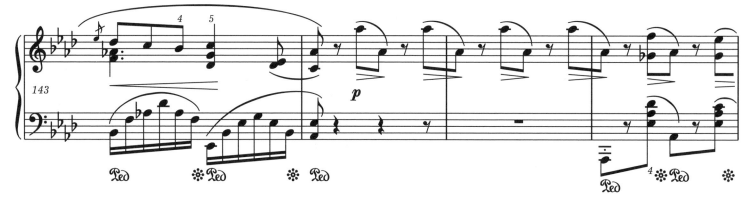

* W t. 150-153 w dwóch egzemplarzach lekcyjnych dodany przez Chopina łuk jak w t. 109-112.
  In bars 150-153 two pupils' copies contain a slur added by Chopin, as in bars 109-112.

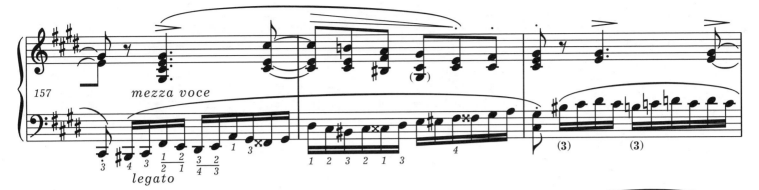

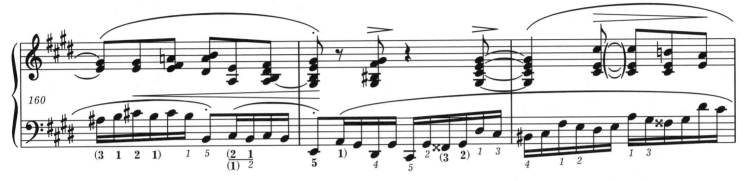

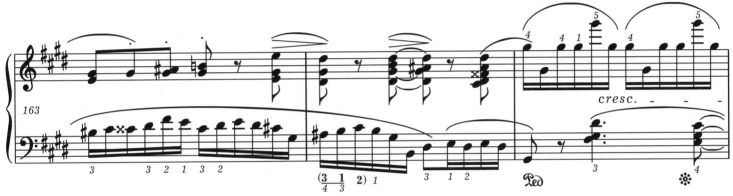

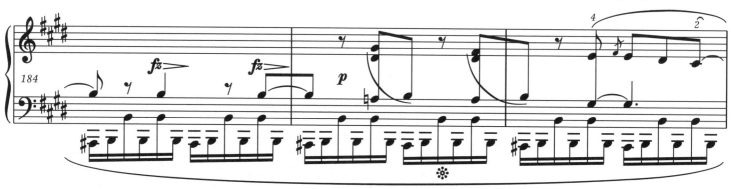

* Dopuszczalny wariant oparty na wcześniejszej wersji:
  A permissible variant, based on the earlier version:

Patrz *Komentarz źródłowy.*
Vide Source Commentary.

PWM-4927

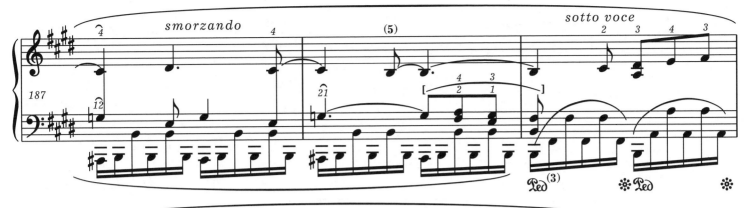

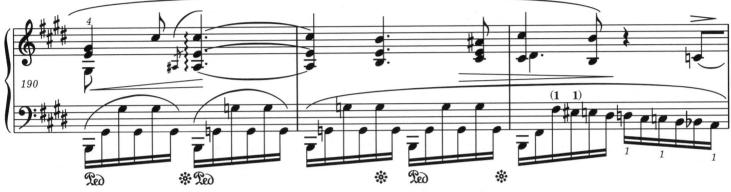

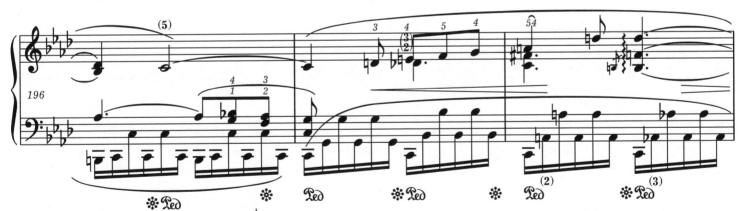

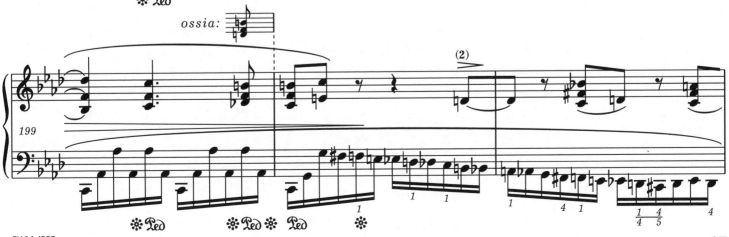

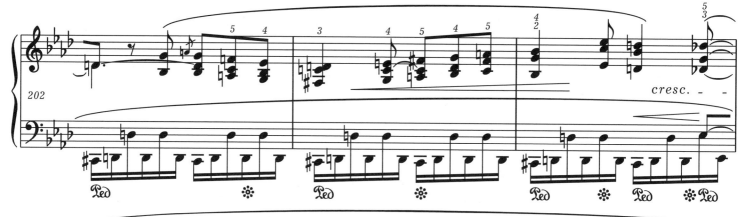

46

PWM-4927

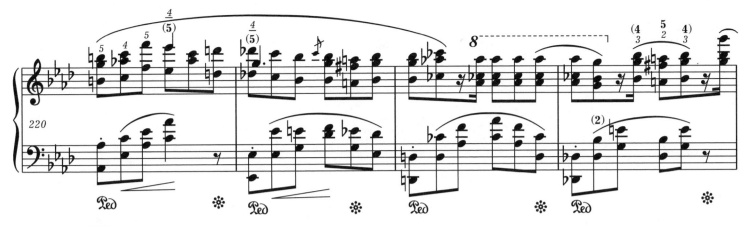

* Dźwięk *as'* należy powtórzyć.
  The note *ab'* should be repeated.

47

Ballade
A Madame Nathaniel de Rothschild

op. 52

Andante con moto

* Dopuszczalny wariant jak w t. 30.
A permissible variant, as in bar 30.

PWM-4927

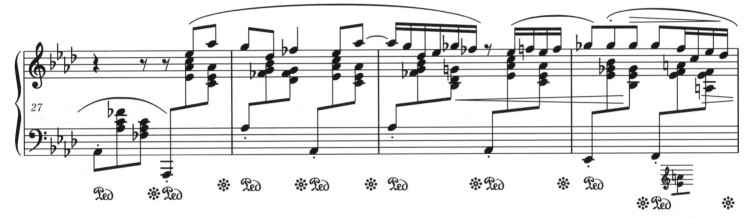

PWM-4927

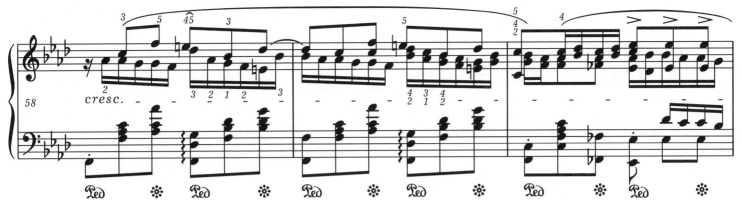

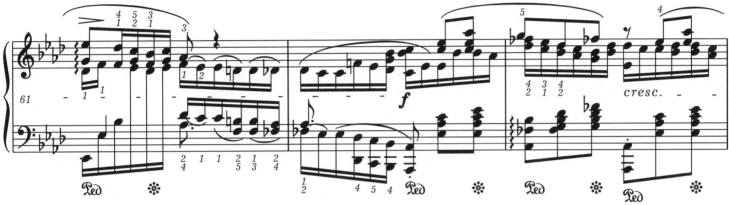

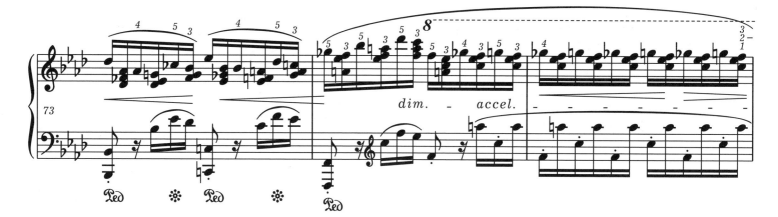

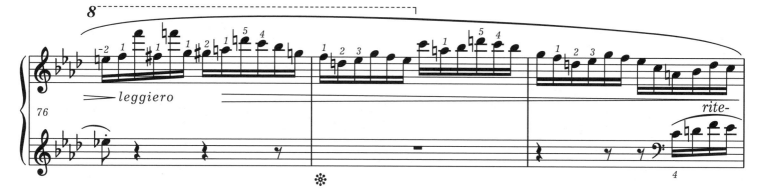

* Patrz *Komentarz źródłowy.*
  Vide Source Commentary.

** Palcowanie Chopina: nad nutami odnosi się do prawej ręki, pod nutami - do lewej.
   Fingering by Chopin: over the notes it refers to the R. H., and below the notes - to the L.H.

PWM-4927

* Wcześniejsza wersja, którą można uważać za wariant:
  An earlier version which should be recognized as a variant:

** Patrz *Komentarz źródłowy.*
   Vide Source Commentary.

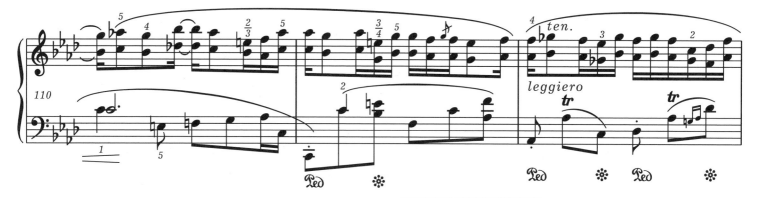

54

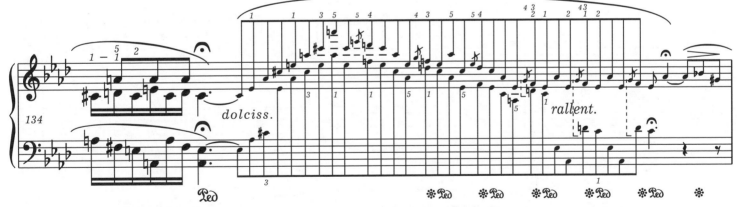

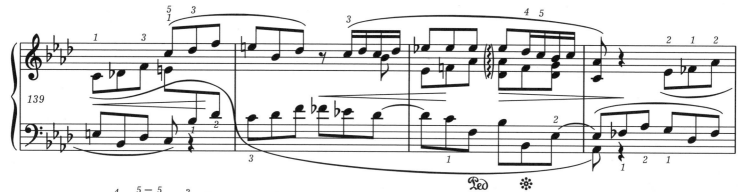

PWM-4927

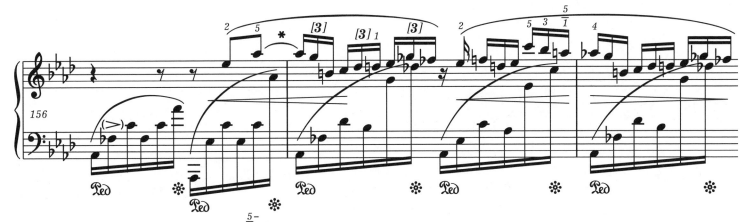

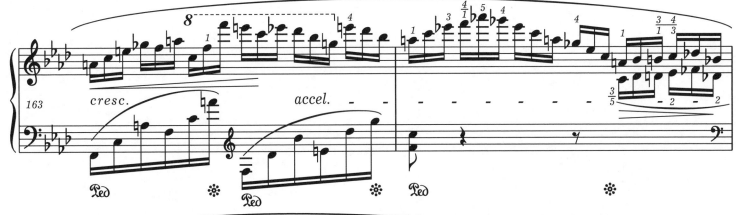

* W jednym ze źródeł, być może omyłkowo, brak łuku przetrzymującego *as²*.
  One of the sources, maybe erroneously, has no tie sustaining the *ab²*.

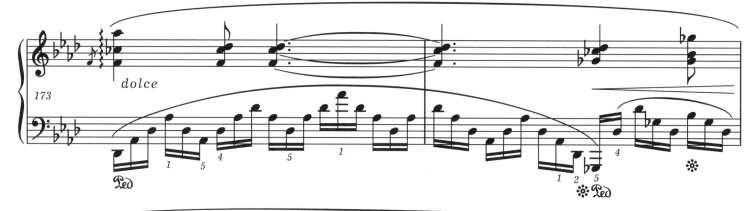

PWM-4927

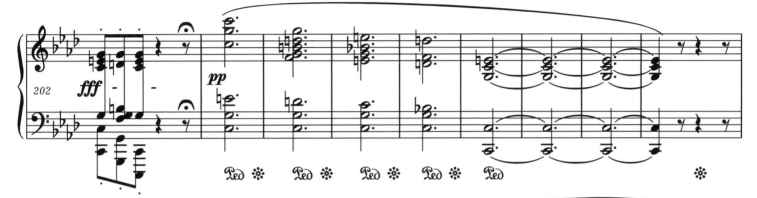

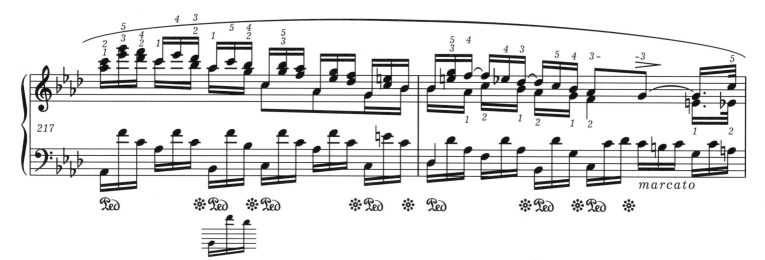

* Autentyczność następującej wersji tej trioli w jednym ze źródeł: nie jest pewna. Patrz *Komentarz źródłowy.*
The authenticity of the following version of this triplet in one of the sources: remains uncertain. *Vide Source Commentary.*

** Patrz *Komentarz wykonawczy.*
Vide Performance Commentary.

PWM-4927

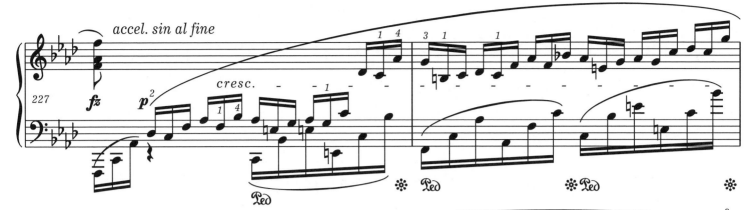

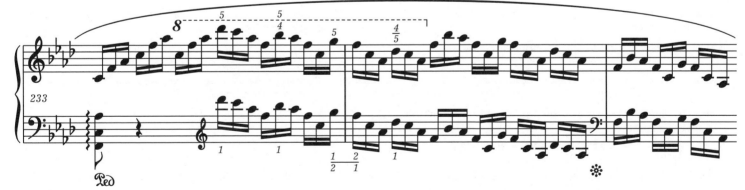

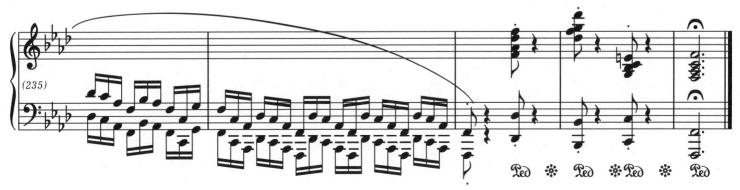

FRYDERYK CHOPIN
BALLADES

Performance Commentary
Source Commentary (abridged)

PERFORMANCE COMMENTARY

Notes on the musical text

The v a r i a n t s marked as *ossia* were given this label by Chopin or were added in his hand to pupils' copies; variants without this designation are the result of discrepancies in the texts of authentic versions or an inability to establish an unambiguous reading of the text.

Minor authentic alternatives (single notes, ornaments, slurs, accents, pedal indications etc.) that can be regarded as variants are enclosed in round brackets (), whilst editorial additions are written in square brackets [].

Pianists who are not interested in editorial questions, and want to base their performance on a single text, unhampered by variants, are recommended to use the music printed in the principal staves, including all the markings in brackets.

Chopin's original fingering is indicated in large bold-type numerals, **1 2 3 4 5**, in contrast to the editors' fingering which is written in small italic numerals *1 2 3 4 5*. Wherever authentic fingering is enclosed in parentheses this means that it was not present in the primary sources but added by Chopin to his pupils' copies.

A general discussion on the interpretation of Chopin's works is to be contained in a separate volume: *The Introduction to the National Edition,* in the section entitled *Problems of Performance.*

Abbreviations: R.H. — right hand, L.H. — left hand.

1. Ballade in G minor, Op. 23

p. 12   *Bar 25* L.H. The start of the trill with grace-notes:

 . *d♯* simultaneously with *g¹* in the R.H.

Bar 32 R.H. The arpeggio should be started together with the octave in the L.H.

p. 14   *Bars 72-75* In order to avoid an excessive mingling of melodic notes and retain complete harmony, which would be ensured by Chopinesque pedalling, the latter can be somewhat modified by a simultaneous application of a "harmonic legato" in the L.H. (fingers sustain the harmonic notes):

p. 16   *Bar 92* On modern pianos this bar is best executed with one pedal since the mingling of melodic notes *e²* and *f²* is less jarring than losing the basic notes *B♭* and *f* while changing the pedal on the third quaver. Pianists with a larger hand span can use the following technique, which makes it possible to retain full harmony and a clean rendering of the melody:

Bar 93 A different fingering of this bar could be the result of the original text:

p. 17   *Bar 113* R.H. Execution of the chord with grace-notes:

Bars 114 and 174 R.H. The melody of the theme should be emphasized:

p. 20   *Bar 166* ***f♯*** on the first note is obtained easier by playing with the R.H.:

p. 21   *Bar 179* R.H. ***tr*** = ∿ .

R.H. Judging by the alignment of the notes in the autograph (reproduced in our edition) and the approximate calculation of rhythmic values, the second half of the bar is best executed as follows:

p. 22   *Bar 193* R.H. Different fingering:

p. 25   *Bar 246* L.H. The arpeggio should be executed in an anticipatory manner i.e. *g¹* simultaneously with *e♭⁴* in the R.H.

Bar 258-259 The marking of the breaking of the octaves first with grace-notes and then with the help of diagonal lines indicates a gradual acceleration of the break, parallel to the *poco ritenuto — accelerando* marking, so that together with the start of bar 260 it would be possible to imperceptibly enter into ideally simultaneous and rapid octaves.

2. Ballade in F major, Op. 38

p. 26   *Bars 19, 21, 41, 93 and 95* R.H.

The first note of the arpeggio (in bar 19 *c¹*) should be struck simultaneously with the appropriate note in the L.H.

p. 31   *Bar 118* A sign to execute *f#* with the L.H. comes from the editors.

p. 33   *Bar 165* L.H. The start of the trill with grace-notes:

D# simultaneously with the first semiquaver in the R.H.

p. 34   *Bars 172 and 176* R.H. Facilitation:

. Analogously in bar 176.

Bars 179 and 183 L.H. Facilitation for a smaller hand:

. Analogously in bar 183.

p. 35   *Bar 197* A pianistically convenient and sonorically expressive realization of the beginning of the bar:

Bar 203 R.H. Simultaneously with the octave in the L.H., the grace-note should be played, and in case the version without the grace-note is selected — the first note of the arpeggio should be struck.

3. Ballade in A flat major, Op. 47

p. 36   *Bars 3 and 39* L.H. The grace-note (or in the variant the first note of the mordent) should be struck simultaneously with the R.H. chord.

Bars 9, 10 and analogously The original pedalling seems to indicate the fact that Chopin wished to retain the sound of the fundamental bass note also in the second half of the bars despite the changing harmonies. On modern pianos the retention of the bass notes without blurring the harmonies can be attained by rapidly changing the pedal in the middle of the bar. The bass notes can be also sustained with the use of a third (sostenuto) pedal.

Bar 14 R.H. Facilitation of the second half of the bar:

Using this facilitation, care should be taken so that the sound effect is close to the sonority resulting from the execution of the octaves in the R.H. alone, as foreseen by Chopin: not too rapidly and with suitable articulation — *legato* for the upper notes and *non legato* for the lower ones.

Bar 22 R.H. In the opinion of the editors the best execution of the chord grace-note is:

p. 37   *Bars 26 and 28* R.H. The start of the trill in bar 26:

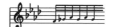

f¹ together with the L.H. chord. Analogously in bar 28.

Bars 29-32 R.H. Execution of trills:

and

p. 40   *Bars 97-98* A different division of chords between two hands:

The arpeggiation of certain chords emulates their execution in the original division into hands (the inclusion of arpeggios in brackets is left to the discretion of the performer).

p. 41   *Bar 136* R.H. The grace-note *eb²* should be struck together with *Eb* in the L.H.

p. 42   *Bar 139* R.H. Playing the lower note of the arpeggio together with the first L.H. semiquaver is more in keeping with Chopin's style.

p. 45   *Bars 189-190 and 197-198* L.H. Facilitation for smaller hands:

Analogously in bars 197-198.

Bars 190 and 198 R.H. The grace-note should be struck simultaneously with the first semiquaver of the second half of the bar in the L.H.

p. 47   *Bars 235 and 236* R.H. The start of the trill in bar 235:

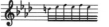

d² together with the L.H. sixth. Analogously in bar 236.

4. Ballade in F minor, Op. 52

p. 48 *Bar 1* R.H. The fact that Chopin placed the marking *legato* between the R.H. voices can denote only a "harmonic legato" — in this case the retention of the notes c^2 as was marked for the accompanying seconds and thirds in bars 2 and 4.

Bars 4, 131 and 132 R.H. The lower note of the arpeggios should be played simultaneously with the L.H.

p. 49 *Bars 38-45* On modern pianos the pedal depressed at the beginning of bars 38 and 42 can be sustained longer (at least by half a bar), and then a pedal changed on each quaver should be added.

p. 51 *Bars 61 and 65* R.H. The arpeggios should be started together with an appropriate L.H. note.

Bar 65 A sign to execute gb^1 with the R.H. comes from the editors.

p. 52 *Bars 74-77* On modern pianos the pedal can be sustained at least a bar longer.

Bars 85 and 93 R.H.  bb together with the L.H. crotchet.

p. 53 *Bar 104* L.H. The depression of the pedal immediately after the third semiquaver makes it possible for even the smallest hand to sustain the $G\sharp$ fundamental bass note without mingling the melodic semitones.

p. 54 *Bars 112 and 114* L.H. The realization of trills in bar 112:

. Analogously in bar 114.

p. 55 *Bar 128* Taking b into the L.H. is an editorial suggestion.

Bar 134 At the end of the cadenza it is possible to retain the sonority of the basis of harmony, the *A-e* fifth, without mingling the notes $c\sharp^1$-d^1-e^1-f^1 with a single pedal:

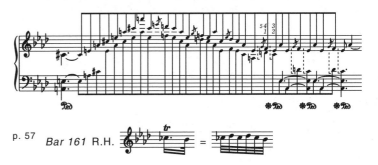

p. 57 *Bar 161* R.H.

p. 58 *Bar 173* R.H. The grace-note f^1 before the arpeggio should be sounded simultaneously with Db in the L.H.

p. 60 *Bar 191 sqq.*

p. 62 *Bars 223 and 225* The Ignaz Friedmann, Alfred Cortot and Alfred Casella editions contain a variant of fingering worthy of recommendation:

Jan Ekier
Paweł Kamiński

SOURCE COMMENTARY /ABRIDGED/

Introductory remarks

The following commentary sets out in an abridged form the principles of editing the musical text of particular works and discusses the most important discrepancies between the authentic sources; furthermore, it draws attention to unauthentic versions which are most frequently encountered in the collected editions of Chopin's music compiled after his death. A separately published *Source Commentary* contains a detailed description of the sources, their filiation, justification of the choice of primary sources, a thorough presentation of the differences between them and a reproduction of characteristic fragments.

Remark to the second edition

This edition of the Ballades took into consideration sources inaccessible during work on the first edition (PWM, Kraków 1967), predominantly: a fragment of the editorial autograph of the *Ballade in F minor*, Op. 52 and copies of different impressions of the first French editions* of all the *Ballades*, making it possible to follow their correction by Chopin. This fact enabled a more certain establishment of the text and the reduction of the number of variants. In comparison to the first edition of *Source Commentaries* (PWM, Kraków 1970), data concerning sources and their filiation have been brought up to date (i.a. the numeration of the impressions of the first editions has been altered).

Abbreviations: R.H. — right hand, L.H. — left hand. The sign → symbolizes a connection between sources; it should be read "and ... based on it".

1. Ballade in G minor, Op. 23

S o u r c e s
A   Autograph/fair-copy (private collection, photocopy in the Chopin Society, Warsaw). **A** served as the basis for the first French edition.
FE1   First French edition, M. Schlesinger (M.S. 1928), Paris VII 1836. **FE1** was based on **A** and contains numerous changes introduced by Chopin during the proof-reading.
FE2   The second impression of **FE1**, VIII 1836, perfunctorily corrected by Chopin.
FE   = **FE1** and **FE2**.
FED   Collection of copies of **FE** belonging to Chopin's pupil Camille Dubois, with annotations by Chopin (Bibliothèque Nationale, Paris), containing fingerings, performance indications, variants and corrections of printing errors.
GE1   First German edition, Breitkopf & Härtel (5706), Leipzig VI 1836. **GE1** repeated (with errors) the **FE1** version, introducing its own revisions. We cannot exclude the possibility that some of the changes in **GE1** come from Chopin.
GE2, GE3, GE4 — further impressions of **GE1**, successively introducing unauthentic changes and supplements.
GE   = **GE1**, **GE2**, **GE3** and **GE4**.
EE   First English edition, Wessel & C° (W & C° 1644), London V 1836. **EE** was based on **FE1** and was not corrected by Chopin.

E d i t o r i a l   P r i n c i p l e s
We have accepted as our basis **FE2** as the last authentic source, compared with **A**.

p. 11   *Bar 1* **A** (→**FE**→**EE**) has **Largo** as the tempo marking. The **Lento** in **GE** could have been added by Chopin to the **FE1** copy serving as the basis for **GE**.

Bar 7 L.H. The top note in **A** (→**FE**→**EE**) is *eb¹*, and in **GE** — *d¹*. This ambiguity gave rise to doubts already during Chopin's

---

lifetime. The **GE** version could be either a revision of this edition (*cf.* commentary to bars 45 and 47) or a variant introduced by Chopin (to avoid parallel fifths in upper voices?, together with **Lento**? — *vide* commentary to bar 1). Long after the death of Chopin, Saint-Saëns stated that he deduced from Liszt's elusive response that Chopin played *d¹*. Nonetheless, apart from such certain sources as **A** and **FE**, twice corrected by Chopin, testimonies of four persons closely connected with Chopin (Marcelina Czartoryska, Friederike Streicher, Ferdinand Hiller and Adolf Gutmann) speak in favour of the version with *eb¹*.

p. 12   *Bar 26-27* R.H. In **FE** (→**GE**, **EE**) the tie which in **A** sustains the minim *d²* to the next bar has been mistakenly deciphered as a phrasing slur and joined to the slur over bars 27-28.

p. 13   *Bars 45 and 47* R.H. Before the first quaver in both bars **GE** has ♯. This is an arbitrary addition made by the reviser of **GE** (*cf.* commentary to the *Ballade in F minor*, Op. 52, bars 164 and 165).

p. 14   *Bar 63* R.H. The last quaver in **GE** is mistakenly *d*. Probably the engraver mistook this bar for one of the similar bars 57, 59 or 61-62 (such errors were committed elsewhere in **GE**: *d¹* instead of *c¹* on the first note of the second half of bar 100 and *e¹* instead of *d¹* on the fourth crotchet in the L.H. in bar 114). The version with *c* in **A** (→**FE**→**EE**) prepares harmony in bar 64 in a manner characteristic for Chopin, avoiding the suspension of the *d* sound, absent in this harmony.

p. 16   *Bar 99* R.H. On the fifth and sixth crotchet **A** has the chord *e¹-a¹-c²*. Chopin removed both *e¹* in the proofs of **FE1** (→**GE**, **EE**).

Bars 103-105 L.H. On the last beat **A** has in each of these bars a rest instead of the chord *e-a-c¹*. We give the version Chopin introduced in the proofs of **FE1** (→**GE**,**EE**). The majority of the later collected editions give an unauthentic compiled version of those bars: bars 103-104 in the original sonority (with a rest) but bar 105 with an arpeggiated chord of the final version.

p. 17   *Bars 119 and 123* R.H. In **A** there are no chromatic signs over the mordents in these bars. In the proofs of **FE1** Chopin added ♯ over 🔀 in bar 123. The majority of the later collected editions, assuming the possibility of an oversight, also added ♯ in bar 119. There are no arguments, however, in favour of an oversight by Chopin. The mordent with the semitone *g²* in bar 119 better corresponds to the scale octave progression in B-minor and the analogous melodic-tonal situation in bar 121. On the other hand, the whole-tonal 🔀 in bar 123 (*g♯²-a♯²*) signalizes modulation changes in that particular bar and following bars.

p. 18   *Bars 126 and 136* **A** has *sempre più animato* in bar 126 and *più vivo* in bar 136. We give the reduced — probably by Chopin — markings in **FE** (→**GE**,**EE**).

Bars 134-135 R.H. **A** has the original version:

Chopin changed it by correcting **FE** (→**GE**,**EE**).

Bar 137 R.H. Before the fifth quaver **A** has ♮, removed by Chopin in the proofs of **FE1** (→**GE**,**EE**).

---

* The inclusion of this group of sources into editorial work was made possible thanks to the research and assistance of Dr. Krzysztof **Grabowski** from Paris.

p. 19 *Bar 145* L.H. The original version of the first half of the bar

in **A**: [musical notation]. Chopin changed it in **FE** (→**GE**,**EE**).

p. 20 *Bar 171* R.H. **A** (→**FE**1→**GE**,**EE**) has a version which we give in the variant. In **FE**2 it was changed into the following:

[musical notation]. The alterations were conducted certainly upon the request of Chopin but it is doubtful whether it was his intention to leave *d²* in the last but one crotchet of the quintuplet. The erroneous double engraving of the shifted note is encountered upon several occasions in the first French editions of Chopin's works (e.g. the *Scherzo in B minor*, Op. 20, bars 135 and 292, the *Polonaise in A*, Op. 40 No. 1, second version, bar 93). Hence in the main text we give a version of **FE**2 corrected by Chopin, emended analogously to bar 170.

p. 21 *Bar 173* R.H. The main text comes from **FE** (→**GE**,**EE**), the variant — from **A**. The crossing-out in **A** testify to Chopin's indecision as regards the two possibilities; similar variants are encountered in his other works (e.g. the *Ballade in A♭*, Op. 47, bars 3 and 39).

p. 22 *Bar 193* R.H. **GE**3 arbitrarily changes the sixth quaver from *e♭²* to *d²*.
R.H. The last quaver in **A** is mistakenly *d¹*. Chopin corrected it to *e♭¹* in the proofs of **FE**1 (→**GE**,**EE**).

Bars 194, 196 and 198 R.H. The accents in the form of short lines, rarely used by Chopin, were written by him into **FE**D.

p. 23 *Bar 214* L.H. At the beginning of the bar **FE** (→**GE**,**EE**) has the *a-c¹-g¹* triad. **A** is not very legible at this point but there are no clear reasons for differentiating this bar and bar 210, with an indubitable four-note chord (with *e♭¹*).

Bar 223 L.H. At the end of this bar **FE** (→**GE**, **EE**) has an *a-d¹* fourth. This is probably an error caused by the indistinct record of this crotchet in **A**. A comparison with the harmonically similar bar 217 and analogous ones speaks in favour of the *a-c¹-d¹* chord.

p. 24 *Bar 229* L.H. The majority of the later collected editions arbitrarily adds *b♭* to the authentic *g* on the last crotchet.

p. 25 *Bar 259* Diagonal lines indicating the breaking of octaves in the second half of the bar (*cf. Performance Commentary*) were omitted in **FE** (→**GE**,**EE**).

2. Ballade in F major, Op. 38

S o u r c e s
A Autograph/fair-copy which served as the basis for the first French edition and then the first English edition (Bibliothèque Nationale, Paris).
GC Copy, probably by Gutmann, which served as the basis for the first German edition (Stiftelsen Musikkulturens Främjande, Stockholm). In **GC** the copyist committed numerous errors and imprecisions. In a probably hurried examination, Chopin introduced a number of supplementations and corrections.
FE1 First French edition, E. Troupenas (T. 925), Paris X 1840. **FE**1 was based on **A**, contained a considerable number of errors (i.a. in slurring) and was not corrected by Chopin.
FE2 The second impression of **FE**1 (the same firm and number), corrected by Chopin.

FE3 The third impression of **FE**1 (the same firm and number), which introduced, above all, numerous and, as a rule, obvious supplementations of accidentals. Chopin most probably did not participate in its production.
FE = **FE**1, **FE**2 and **FE**3.
FED As in the *Ballade in G minor*, Op. 23.
FES,**FE**J — collections of pupils' copies of **FE** with annotations by Chopin, containing fingering, performance directives, variants, and corrections of printing errors.
    FES — collection belonging to Chopin's pupil, Jane Stirling (Bibliothèque Nationale, Paris),
    FEJ — collection belonging to Chopin's sister, Ludwika Jędrzejewiczowa (Chopin Society, Warsaw).
EE First English edition, Wessel & C° (W & C° 3182), London X 1840. **EE** was based on **A** and was not corrected by Chopin.
GE1 First German edition, Breitkopf & Härtel (6330), Leipzig X 1840. **GE**1 was based on **GC** and was not corrected by Chopin. There are copies of **GE**1 with different prices on the covers.
GE2 Second German edition (the same firm and number), after 1852, with small adjustments of the text of **GE**1.
GE = **GE**1 and **GE**2.

E d i t o r i a l   P r i n c i p l e s
We have based our text on **A** and taken into consideration changes introduced by Chopin to **GC** and **FE**2 as well as his additions to pupils' copies.

p. 26 *Bars 26-27* R.H. Some of the later collected editions arbitrarily tie *g¹* notes over bar-line.

p. 27 *Bars 37-38* R.H. Analogously to bars 91-92 some of the later collected editions arbitrarily add notes *e¹* on the last quaver of bar 37 and at the beginning of bar 38.

p. 28 *Bar 53* R.H. The original beginning of the bar was:

[musical notation]. Already in **A** (→**FE**,**EE**) Chopin altered it to:

[musical notation]. In **GC** (→**GE**) Chopin changed this second version to the text which we present.

Bar 54 L.H. On the fourth quaver some of the later collected editions arbitrarily changed the *A₁-A* octave to *C-c*.

p. 30 *Bar 93* R.H. **A** (→**FE**,**EE**) has no arpeggio which is found in **GC** (→**GE**), probably added by Chopin.

Bar 98-99 R.H. **A** (→**FE**,**EE**) has no tie sustaining *g♭¹*. Chopin added it in **GC** (→**GE**).

Bars 101,107,126 and 132 R.H. In the second half of the bars it is difficult to ascertain the sonority of the third in the lower voice intended by Chopin. **A** (→**FE**1,**EE**) has the version presented in our edition. In **GC** (→**GE**) Chopin added ♮ in bar 126, changing *b♭-d¹* to *b-d¹*. In the proofs of **FE**2 Chopin added ♮ in bar 132, changing *e¹-g¹* to *e♭¹-g¹*. Below we present a list of thirds (major or minor) in particular sources:

bar	101	107	126	132
1. **A**	major	minor	major	minor
2. **GC**	major	minor	minor	minor
3. **FE**2	major	minor	major	major

This table shows that:
— none of the sources contains an identical version in all bars
— the presumption that while correcting **GC** or **FE**2 Chopin intended to unify those passages leads to a contradiction since in **GC** he altered the major third to a minor one, and in

FE2 the minor third to a major one
— accepting that a differentiation of those bars corresponds to Chopin's intentions, we must recognise version 1 as the most perfect one. The remaining versions are probably the result of Chopin's errors due to a hurried and fragmentary proof-reading of those greatly similar passages.
Some of the later collected editions, whose point of departure is the second version, arbitrarily change the major third in bar 101 to a minor one, and give a reduced, identical version in all four bars.

Bar 105 R.H. In the second half of the bar some of the later collected editions arbitrarily add *ab¹* to the *f¹* of the lower voice.

Bar 106 R.H. The main text comes from **FE**2 in which Chopin corrected the incomplete and erroneous version of **FE**1. The variant is the **A** version; it is not clear whether it was Chopin's intention to sustain *gb¹* (as in **EE**) or to repeat it (**GC**→**GE**).

Bars 110-111 R.H. At the end of bar 110 **A** (→**FE**1,**EE**) has octaves *g#²-g#³* and *a²-a³*. Chopin supplemented them with *e³* notes both in **GC** (**GE** mistakenly reads *f³* in the last quaver) and in the proofs of **FE**2. This corrected version, in which the passage from a four-note chord in the middle of the bar to an octave in bar 111, rendered smooth thanks to three-note chords, is presented by us as the main version. In the variant, however, we cite the original **A** version since the false relation between *e³* in bar 110 and the Eb octaves in bar 111 is less audible. Some of the later collected editions arbitrarily add *eb³* to the octave at the beginning of bar 111.

Bars 111-112 L.H. Octaves *Bb₁-Bb* are tied between the bars in **A** (→**GC**→**GE**, →**FE**1,**EE**). In the proofs of **FE**2 Chopin removed the ties, probably in order to achieve rhythmic analogy with bars 136-137. The ties were subsequently restored in **FE**3, but probably not by Chopin himself but by the reviser who in this impression checked the slurs and ties according to **A**. We thus present the **FE**2 version, undoubtedly corrected by Chopin, as the main version.

p. 31 *Bars 123-124 and 129-130* R.H. The majority of later collected editions joins notes *f¹* in bars 123-124 and *bb¹* in bars 129-130 analogously to bars 98-99 and 104-105. Nothing, however, indicates that Chopin wanted a strict analogy between bars 99-108 and 124-133.

Bars 125-126 L.H. Sources do not lengthen *G* to bar 126 (no note and tie). This is certainly Chopin's oversight connected with the fact that bar 126 begins a new page in **A**. *Cf.* analogous bars 101,107 and 132.

Bar 133 R.H. In **A** (→**GC**→**GE**, →**FE**1,**EE**) the semiquaver is only the *g¹-g²* octave. In the proofs of **FE**2 Chopin supplemented it with the note *c²*.

Bar 139 R.H. **FE** overlooks *bb¹* in the third chord of the bar.

p. 32 *Bar 148* R.H. The upper note in the first semiquaver in **A** (→**FE**,**EE**) is *e¹* (our main text). In **GC** this note was altered but it is difficult to say whether the mistakenly written *f¹* was corrected to *e¹* by Chopin or the copyist, or, on the contrary, whether Chopin altered the correctly copied *e¹* to *f¹* (as understood in **GE**, our variant). Numerous errors and imprecision of the copyist as well as the absence of an accent over this note, while the *f¹* four semiquavers earlier and later are accented, speak in favour of the first possibility (*e¹*).
L.H. **FE** overlooks ties sustaining the *G#₁-G#* octave.

p. 33 *Bars 169 and 173* R.H. There is no accidental before the lower note of the first sixth in the second half of the bar in **A** as well as in **GC** and **FE**, both corrected by Chopin. This means that Chopin wanted to have *d#¹* in bar 169 and *d#²* in bar 173. The revisers of **EE** in bar 169 and **GE** in bar 173 added ♮ next to those notes, perhaps misled by an unnecessary natural next to *b²* in bar 173.

p. 34 *Bar 173* L.H. In **A** (→**GC**→**GE**, →**FE**1,**EE**) the second quaver is the *c¹-f¹* fourth. This error was corrected by Chopin in the proofs of **FE**2.

p. 35 *Bar 196* Before the notes *bb, bb², bb³* in the second half of the bar **A** (→**GC**→**GE**1, →**FE**1→**FE**2) has no accidentals and thus the flats from the first half of the bar are binding. The crossing-out of the sign, visible in **A** and GC, before the lower note of the L.H. chord (**GC** shows that this was ♭) also proves that Chopin checked the correctness of the script in both manuscripts. The revisers of **EE**, **FE**3 and **GE**2 added naturals before these notes (*b, b²* and *b³*), making this chord similar to two previous ones (in bars 195-196). The authentic version of the chord (*f-ab-bb-d*) avoids a mechanical repetition of a diminished seventh chord in three parts of the sequence; in this version, the climax chord in bar 197 is more expressive thanks to three notes, new in relation to the previous chord.

Bars 202-204 The several versions of the end of the *Ballade* testify to Chopin's undecidedness. In chronological order they are:
1. The original version in **A**

2. The later version in **A** (→**EE**), added by Chopin underneath the crossed out first version

This version was copied in **GC** where Chopin then modified it; it is also contained in **FE**1 (with a mistaken *c¹* instead of *d¹* in bar 203).
3. The **GC** version altered by Chopin

This version was adopted in **GE**, correcting the lower note in bar 203 and adding a mistaken tie joining the grace-note and minim *g#*.
4. The **FE**2 version corrected by Chopin

These four versions are divided into two pairs with a different range of the chords: "open" versions 1 and 3 and "close" versions 2 and 4. It is highly probable that it was precisely the wavering between the "open" ending, corresponding to the whole *Ballade*, and the "close" one, which did not transcend beyond the atmosphere of the few last bars (from *tempo primo*), that was the cause of so many changes in this fragment.

Among the "open" versions, version 3 is later than version 1 but it contains a mistaken pitch (C_1 instead of E_1 in bar 203) and three distinct stylistic lapses:

— the doubling of the leading-note $g\sharp$-$g\sharp^1$ in bar 203
— the absence of the resolution of $g\sharp$ to a
— a double-octave leap of the bass from e in bar 202 to E_1 in bar 203.

The following conclusion comes to mind: inasmuch as the very f a c t of corrections conducted by Chopin in GC is the expression of his unquestioned intention to pass from a "close" version to an "open" one, the r e s u l t of those corrections, which is probably due to the hurried manner of their introduction, cannot be acknowledged as definitive. The "open" version, which best reflects Chopin's intention, is, therefore, the version 1.

Among the "close" versions, version 4, introduced by Chopin into the proofs of **FE**2 in place of version 2, should be regarded as definitive.

Our edition takes into consideration Chopin's uncertainty by presenting two basic versions (1 and 4). For the main text we have accepted the "open" version (enhanced with a variant grace-note, characteristic for Chopin, and added in GC) which corresponds to the *Ballade* as a whole, since while changing the "close" version in the proofs of **FE**2 Chopin could have felt constrained in introducing in print excessively far reaching alterations.

3. Ballade in A flat major, Op. 47

Sources

A   Autograph/fair-copy (lost, photocopy in the Chopin Society in Warsaw). Fontana used **A** to make a copy intended as the basis for the first French edition. Subsequently, **A** served as the basis for the first German edition.

[FC] Lost copy by Fontana, made upon the basis of **A**. **[FC]** served as the basis for the first French edition. Superficial proof-reading by Chopin is not excluded.

SC   Copy by Saint-Saëns (Bibliothèque Nationale, Paris), made upon the basis of **[FC]** compared with the first French edition. **SC** makes possible an almost complete reconstruction of **[FC]**.

GE1 First German edition, Breitkopf & Härtel (6652), Leipzig I 1842. **GE**1 was based on **A** and was not corrected by Chopin.

GE2 Second impression of **GE**1 (the same firm and number) after 1870, correcting part of the errors in **GE**1 and introducing a number of changes (some according to **FE**, others arbitrarily).

FE1 First French edition, M. Schlesinger (M.S. 3486), Paris XI 1841. **FE**1 was based on **[FC]** and corrected by Chopin.

FE2 Second impression of **FE**1 (the same firm and number), also corrected by Chopin.

FE   = **FE**1 and **FE**2.

FED As in the *Ballade in G minor*, Op. 23.

FES, **FE**J — as in the *Ballade in F*, Op. 38.

FESch — a copy of **FE** with annotations by Chopin, from a collection belonging to Chopin's pupil, Marie de Scherbatoff (Houghton Library, New York). Contains fingering, a variant and a corrected printing error.

EE   First English edition, Wessel & Stapleton (W & S 5299), London I 1842. **EE** was based on **FE**2 and was not corrected by Chopin.

Editorial Principles

We have based our text on **FE**2 as the last authentic source compared with **A** in order to eliminate the numerous errors and oversights of the engravers. We take into consideration Chopin's annotations in four pupils' copies.

p. 36   *Bars 3 and 39* L.H. In **A** (→[**FC**],**GE**) the note bb starting the second half of the bar is marked with a mordent (which in bar 39 is indicated as *tr*). **FE**1 contains no ornaments, a fact which Chopin corrected in **FE**2 (→**EE**), adding grace-notes which make it possible to achieve the legato in this phrase easier than do the mordents. This type of variants is encountered several times in Chopin's works e.g. in the *Ballade in G minor*, Op. 23, bar 173 or the *Mazurka in C♯ minor*, Op. 41 No. 4, bars 97-101.

Bars 6-7 L.H. In **A** a tie sustaining the eb is found only in bar 7 which starts the new line. The absence of the tie in bar 6 could be Chopin's oversight (this is the way it was understood by [**FC**]→**FE**→**EE**). It cannot be completely excluded that it was the tie in bar 7 which was introduced mistakenly (it is absent in **GE**); a similar Chopin's error — see *Source Commentary* to the *Fantaisie* op. 49, bars 182-183.

Bar 15 L.H. **FE** has an erroneous rhythm |♩ 𝄿 ♫ 𝄾 |. This mistake was corrected by Chopin in **FE**S and **FE**J.

Bar 21 L.H. The last chord in **FE**1 is f-ab-c^1-f^1. Correcting this error, **FE**2 mistakenly left only the octave f-f^1.

p. 38   *Bar 46* L.H. Instead of c^2-eb^2 **FE** (→**EE**) mistakenly has ab^1-c^2.

Bars 47-49 The *ossia* variant was added by Chopin in **FE**J.

p. 39   *Bar 71* R.H. The main text comes from **A** (→[**FC**],**GE**1), the variant — from **FE** (→**EE**,**GE**2). We give priority to the **A** version since it is not certain whether the ab^1 in **FE** was added in proof-reading by Chopin himself (it is possible that an error was committed by the engraver), while the authenticity of the **A** version does not give rise to doubts.

Bar 74 L.H. On the last quaver we give the fourth ab-db^1, as in **A** (→[**FC**],**GE**). In **FE** (→**EE**) there is an added f. This note has no natural continuation in the next bar (in contrast to bars 76-77 where it passes to e), in this way deforming the line bb-ab-g-ab-bb-ab-g-f-e of the lower chord notes in bars 73-77. Probably the engraver of **FE** mistook this bar for bar 76.

Bar 83 L.H. It does not follow clearly from the script of **A** whether the last chord is to have three notes (eb-ab-eb^1), as was interpreted by **GE**, or four (with c^1), as it is recorded in [**FC**] (→**FE**→**EE**).

Bar 86 L.H. **FE** (→**EE**) overlooks ab in the grace-note chord.

Bar 87 We give the octaves on the fourth quaver according to **A** (→[**FC**],**GE**). The notes ab and ab^2 were added in **FE** (→**EE**). This is probably an error of the engraver, suggested by the continuum of previous chords. In **A** Chopin crossed out the c^2-ab^2-c^3 chord in the R.H. and replaced it with an empty octave.

Bar 93 L.H. At the beginning of the bar, **A** (→[**FC**],**GE**) has only the lower C. In the proofs of **FE**1 (→**EE**) Chopin added c.

p. 40   *Bar 99* The rhythmic record of this bar in the sources is not clear. **A** (→[**FC**]→**FE**→**EE**) contains the following script:

Our attention is drawn to the following discrepancies between rhythmic values and the graphic arrangement:
— in **A** the *ab-ab¹* octave ascribed to the third quaver of the bar is located distinctly in the middle of the bar (on the fourth quaver)
— the direction of the stems in the R.H. suggests that the *b-d¹* third comprises a second voice, filling the *ab-ab¹* octave. Basic doubt is produced, therefore, by the moment of striking the *ab-ab¹* octave — on the third or fourth quaver of the bar. Two solutions come to mind:
1. With the assumption that the proper localisation of particular touches in the bar is described by the rhythmic values, the *ab-ab¹* octave coincides with the t h i r d quaver of the bar. This solution is dictated by the following arguments:
— Chopin's script does not contain an obvious error and was proof-read by him in **A** (⅂ on the fifth quaver of the bar was clearly added later); this fact explains the appearance of the described discrepancies
— Chopin did not alter the rhythm either in [**FC**] or in **FE** or in any of the four pupils' copies
— it could have been Chopin's intention to achieve a rhythmic and expressive differentiation of bars 99 and 101 (the syncopation in bar 99 would correspond to syncopations in bars 88-94); a similar arrangement of rhythms is encountered in the *Ballade in G minor*, Op. 23, bars 167 and 169
— despite the fact that the *ab-ab¹* octave was not sustained to the end of the bar, the direction of the stems clearly indicates a two-voice treatment of the R.H part. This is the version we present in the main text.
2. With the assumption that a proper localisation of particular touches in the bar is determined by the graphic arrangement of **A**, it is necessary to correct the values of the rests; this will lead to the version, presented in the variant, in which the *ab-ab¹* octave is struck on the f o u r t h quaver of the bar. This solution is favoured by:
— the way of distribution and the rhythmic values of n o t e s in **A**; this suggestion is so distinct that **GE**, based on it, changed the quaver rests on the second quaver of the bar to crotchet rests
— the rhythmic analogy with bar 101.

Bars 99-100 and 101-102 R.H. The text without ties sustaining melodic sounds comes from **A** (→[**FC**]→**FE**→**EE**, →**GE**1). The *ossia* variants given in the footnote come from **FE**D (bars 99-100) and **FE**Sch (bars 101-102). The variant in bars 99-100 has two forms corresponding to two possibilities of interpreting the rhythm in bar 99. In the first — the rhythmic value of the upper *ab¹* had to be corrected. It must be stressed that in **FE**S and **FE**J the ties have not been added in any of the two passages, and that Chopin did not add ties in two places simultaneously in any of the pupils' copies. The introduction of two ties in **GE**2 was an arbitrary revision, adopted by the majority of the later collected editions.

Bars 100-101 R.H. Some of the later collected editions arbitrarily join *eb¹* notes.

Bar 101-102 L.H. The tie joining both *eb¹* was overlooked in [**FC**] (→**FE**→**EE**). This error was adopted by some of the later collected editions, with an arbitrary change from *eb¹* to *e¹* at the beginning of bar 102.

Bars 102-103 R.H. The tie joining both *g¹* was overlooked in [**FC**] (→**FE**→**EE**).

Bar 107 L.H. The last quaver in the sources is the chord *d-g-b*. The analogous bar 56 contains a *g-b* third, and in bar 60 Chopin crossed out the lower note in a previously written triad in **A**. In this situation, it seems highly probable that in bar 107 Chopin did not correct the triad owing to carelessness

(when proof-reading Chopin quite often missed one of the recurring similar passages).

Bars 109-112 and 150-153 L.H. Chopin could not decide how to mark the tenor voice distinctive in those bars. In **A** he originally wrote accents between the notes of the L.H. intervals but then crossed them out, recognising that the accents-diminuendos between staves were sufficient. However, in print, with greater spaces in between the staves than in **A**, this proved to be unclear for the performers and in pupils' copies Chopin added suitable accents (in **FE**D) or slurs (**FE**S and **FE**J).

p. 41 *Bar 121* L.H. At the beginning of the bar **GE** contains a mistaken octave *Eb₁-Eb*.

Bar 122 L.H. Certain later collected editions arbitrarily change the top notes of the chords to *g¹* and *ab¹*.

Bar 125 L.H. In the last chord [**FC**] (→**FE**→**EE**) overlooks the note *db¹*.

Bar 132 L.H. The main text comes from **A** (→[**FC**],**GE**), and the variant — from **FE** (→**EE**). The **FE** version is most probably a simplified correction of a printing error (presumably, the third quaver was originally completely omitted).

p. 42 *Bar 137* This bar was overlooked in **GE**.

Bar 138 R.H. The first chord in **A** has the mistaken value of a quaver.

Bar 140 R.H. **GE**2 arbitrarily ties the *ab²-ab³* octaves.

Bars 143-144 The bars in **A** (→[**FC**],**GE**) are linked as follows:

Chopin simplified this in the proofs of **FE**1 (→**EE**).

p. 43 *Bar 157* R.H. In **A** (→[**FC**],**GE**) the chord on the third quaver of the bar has no *e¹*. Chopin added this note in the proofs of **FE**1 (→**EE**).

Bar 158 R.H. In **A** (→**GE**) the note *g#* appears on the fourth quaver. It is difficult to say whether its absence in [**FC**] (→**FE** →**EE**) is an oversight of the copyist or a correction by Chopin.

Bars 160-161 R.H. The tie joining both *b* was overlooked in [**FC**] (→**FE**→**EE**) and in **GE** it was reproduced imprecisely.

Bar 162 R.H. It is not clear whether Chopin wished to repeat or sustain the chord on the fourth quaver of the bar. **A** (→**GE**1) and **FE** (→**EE**) do not have ties, which, however, appeared in [**FC**] (→**SC**) and have been added by Chopin in **FE**D. Stylistically both versions are possible since this motif appears in the *Ballade* in both forms.

p. 44 *Bar 173* R.H. Some of the later collected editions arbitrarily give the triad *c#²-e²-g#²* as the ninth semiquaver.

Bar 176 In the main text we give the version introduced by Chopin in the proofs of **FE**2 (→**EE**). The variant is basically a version of **A** (→[**FC**],**GE**); only on the third semiquaver in the R.H. did we remove the note *b¹* — similarly to the **FE**2 version (apparently, this simplification of the chord, rather awkward in high tempo, can be treated as independent of the remaining changes in this bar).

Bar 178 R.H. The majority of the later collected editions gives $c\#^2$ instead of the authentic $g\#^2$ as the fourth semiquaver. It seems worthwhile to draw attention to the association of the span of the R.H. figures with the span of the L.H. chords: at the end of bar 173 the octave $c\#^3$-$c\#^4$ is accompanied by the chord $c\#^1$-e^1-$g\#^1$-$c\#^2$ and in bar 178 the eleventh $g\#^2$-$c\#^4$ is accompanied by the chord $g\#$-$c\#^1$-e^1-$c\#^2$.

L.H. FC ($\rightarrow$**FE**$\rightarrow$**EE**) overlooks the note $c\#^1$ in the chord on the third quaver of the bar.

Bar 179 L.H. **A** ($\rightarrow$[**FC**],**GE**) has the $F\#$-$f\#$ octave on the third quaver. Chopin transferred it an octave higher in the proofs of **FE**1 ($\rightarrow$**EE**).

p. 45

Bars 195-196 R.H. At the beginning of bar 196 **A** ($\rightarrow$[**FC**],**GE**) has a rest in the upper voice. In the proofs of **FE**1 ($\rightarrow$**EE**) Chopin changed it to a b-d^1 third (tied to the previous one).

Bar 199 R.H. In **A** the lengthening dots next to the second chord have been overlooked.

R.H. Next to the lower sound of the last chord in **FED** Chopin altered ♭ to ♮. We give this version as *ossia*.

Bar 200 R.H. In the first half of the bar **A** ($\rightarrow$[**FC**]$\rightarrow$**FE**1, $\rightarrow$**GE**) has the following version: . We accept the version introduced by Chopin in the proofs of **FE**2 ($\rightarrow$**EE**).

p. 46

Bar 203 R.H. In the proofs of **FE**1 ($\rightarrow$**EE**) Chopin added a sustained note c^1 on the fourth quaver of the bar.

Bar 211 R.H. **A** has the f^1-f^2 octave on the second quaver; we also see that Chopin crossed out the inner sound. This procedure proved to be unclear for readers of **A** since both **GE** and [**FC**] ($\rightarrow$**FE**$\rightarrow$**EE**) have the chord f^1-d^2-f^2 at this point.

Bar 213 L.H. **A** ($\rightarrow$[**FC**]) has a four-note chord on the third quaver. In it both **GE** and **FE** ($\rightarrow$**EE**) overlook the note eb^1.

Bar 214 L.H. **A** ($\rightarrow$[**FC**],**GE**) has an eb^1-ab^1-c^2 chord on the fourth quaver. In the proofs of **FE**1 ($\rightarrow$**EE**) Chopin removed the note ab^1.

R.H. In **A** the fifth quaver is written rather indistinctly and it is not clear whether ab^3 is included in it or not. **GE** has only c^4, and [**FC**] ($\rightarrow$**FE**$\rightarrow$**EE**) has the ab^3-c^4 third.

Bar 215 R.H. The note g^3 in the first chord in **A** ($\rightarrow$**GE**) is sustained by a tie but not distinguished as a dotted crotchet. We correct this imprecision of notation. [**FC**] ($\rightarrow$**FE**$\rightarrow$**EE**) omits the tie joining both g^3.

Bar 216 The main text comes from **FE** ($\rightarrow$**EE**) where it was introduced by Chopin in his proofs of **FE**1 (visible traces of changes in print). The variant is a version of **A** ($\rightarrow$**GE**). SC has the same rhythm as **FE** but the manner of notation testifies to the fact that Saint–Saëns added this rhythm to the **A** version i.e. that [**FC**] had the **A** version.

Bars 219 and 221 R.H. Some of the later collected editions arbitrarily add ties sustaining the crotchet g^2 (as in bar 215). The repetition of g^2 in those bars is connected with a harmonic context in the L.H., different from bar 215.

p. 47

Bars 228-229 R.H. The bars in **A** ($\rightarrow$[**FC**],**GE**) are linked as follows: . Chopin altered this in the proofs of **FE**1 ($\rightarrow$**EE**).

4. Ballade in F minor, Op. 52

S o u r c e s

AI   A 79-bar fragment of an autograph of the first edition of the *Ballade*, in the original 6/4 metre (private collection, photocopy in the Chopin Society, Warsaw).

[**A**1], [**A**2] – the lost first and second of the three autographs which served as bases for first editions.

A3   Fragment, containing 136 bars, of the chronologically last autograph/fair-copy (Bodleian Library, Oxford), intended as the basis for the first German edition. **A**3 was partially copied from [**A**1], and partially from [**A**2]; it also contains improvements and errors which are absent in all earlier autographs.

[**A**3] Lost end fragment of **A**3.

FE1   First French edition, M. Schlesinger (M.S. 3957), Paris XII 1843. **FE**1 was based on [**A**1] and was most probably corrected by Chopin.

FE2   Second impression of **FE**1 (the same firm and number). Several small changes introduced in **FE**2 could be the outcome of its superficial review by Chopin.

FE   = **FE**1 and **FE**2.

FEJ As in the *Ballade in F*, Op. 38.

EE   First English edition, Wessel & C° (W & C° 5305), London III 1844. **EE** was based on [**A**2] and was not corrected by Chopin; it contains numerous errors.

GE   First German edition, Breitkopf & Härtel (7001), Leipzig XI 1843. **GE** reproduces with errors the text of **A**3 and [**A**3]; it was not corrected by Chopin.

E d i t o r i a l   P r i n c i p l e s

We have based our text on **A**3 and, from bar 137, on **GE**, compared with **FE** and **EE**.

p. 48

Bars 1-2 and 4 **GE** arbitrarily simplifies Chopin's notation, omitting *legato* in bar 1, stems and beams distinguishing the R.H. lower voice in bars 2 and 4, and transferring the L.H. motif in bars 1-2 to the lower staff. This distorted notation was repeated in the majority of the later collected editions.

Bar 1-5 R.H. Dynamic markings in parentheses come from **FE**.

Bar 7 R.H. In the first half of the bar **A**3 ($\rightarrow$**GE**) mistakenly repeats the second half of bar 6. **FE**1 also contains an error: f^1-c^2 on the fourth semiquaver. The correct text is found in **EE** and **FE**2.

Bars 16 and 30 L.H. The sonority of the second quaver in bar 16 and the fifth quaver in bar 30 gives rise to doubt. In bar 16 all sources have the eb^1-f^1-a^1 chord but in bar 30 it occurs only in **AI** and **EE**, while **FE** and **A**3 ($\rightarrow$**GE**) have the eb^1-a^1 interval. In **A**3 it is clear that in bar 30 Chopin crossed out the f^1 in the originally written chord. Since those bars constitute part of double-bar phrases, otherwise completely identical, it seems that it was not the intention of Chopin to differentiate this detail of the accompaniment. Two hypotheses come to mind:
— by crossing out f^1 while looking through **A**3 Chopin mistook bar 30 for one of similar bars (21 or 36); therefore, the version concurrent with his intention would be the one which ignores this crossing-out and which is as a whole and without errors recorded in [**A**2] ($\rightarrow$**EE**, our main text). In this version, the presence of the three- or two-note chord is connected with the preceding harmonic context: in bars 16 and 30 the first, from several bars appearance of the bass F is accompanied by a three-note chord while bars 21 and 36 (as well as 56 and 150), which end the several-bars fragments based on F as the pedal point, have a two-note one;
— Chopin resigned completely from three-note chords in these passages, and bar 16 remained uncorrected due to carelessness (when proof-reading Chopin quite often missed one of the recurring similar passages); we take this possibility into consideration as a variant.

p. 50

Bars 43-44 R.H. The main text comes from **FE** and **EE**, the variant — from **A**3 (→**GE**). Although the absence of ties in **A**3 could be an oversight on the part of Chopin, both versions are musically justified:

— in a sustention of the chord, the four-bar phrases which start in the middle of bars 38 and 42 are rhythmically analogous

— in a repetition of the chord, there come into being two pairs of rhythmically corresponding bars — bars 38 and 40 and bars 42 and 44.

Bar 46 L.H. On the second quaver **GE** mistakenly has an additional c^1.

Bar 48 L.H. The main text comes from **A**I, **EE** and **A**3 (→**GE**), and the variant — from **FE**. In the main version the consistent use of chords ensures bars 47-49 a uniform sonority. In the variant, the repetition in bar 48 of intervals from bar 46 makes it possible for the harmony of the first half of bar 50, which constitutes a turning point of the harmonic progression in bars 46-53, to appear more distinctly.

Bar 51 L.H. On the second quaver **A**I, **FE** and **EE** have the chord ab-eb^1-gb^1. We accept the version of **A**3 (→**GE**) in which the chords on the second and third quavers have two notes in common, as in neighbouring figures.

Bar 55 R.H. Some of the later collected editions arbitrarily change the lower note of the initial chord from eb^1 to gb^1.

Bar 56 L.H. In the last chord **FE** mistakenly omits eb^1. Cf. bars 16, 21 and analogous ones.

p. 51

Bar 58 R.H. Sources differ as regards the sonority of the third and fourth quaver of the bar. **A**I has a strictly two-part version:

In [**A**1] (→**FE**) Chopin supplemented it:

Next, in [**A**2] (→**EE**):

and in **A**3 (→**GE**, the version accepted in our edition) Chopin successively resigned from three-note chords by returning to a strict two-part texture, but with a line of the lower voice modified in comparison to previous versions.

Bar 59 R.H. **FE** has c^1-bb^1 as the first semiquaver of the lower voice.

Bar 65 R.H. We give the second half of the bar according to **A**I and **EE**. Also **A**3 (→**GE**) has a similar version, which differs only because the a^1 note in the chord is not lengthened to a dotted crotchet. **FE** contains the following version:

. The lower note of the chord (gb^1) could be an error made by the engraver. The authenticity of note a^1 repeated on the last but one semiquaver does not give rise to doubts but its absence in **EE** and **A**3 probably signifies that Chopin ultimately resigned from it.

Bar 68 R.H. **GE** mistakenly ties notes a^1 in the two first quavers.

Bar 72 R.H. In the chord on the second semiquaver of the second half of the bar **FE** and **EE** have eb^1 instead of db^1

which is found in **A**I and **A**3 (→**GE**). The **FE** and **EE** version could be an engravers' error, possibly committed under the impact of the previous chord (Chopin wrote notes of seconds one over the other, and not diagonally next to each other). This is the reason why we accept db^1 which appears in both extant manuscripts, and which makes the cb^1-db^1 second sound in all the chords of the second half of the bar, analogously to the bb-cb^1 second from the first half.

Bars 72-73 R.H. Some of the later collected editions arbitrarily change the last but one semiquaver in bar 72 from bb^1 to bbb^1. Others moreover alter the middle notes of chords: in bar 72 on the eighth and tenth semiquaver from db^1 to ebb^1, and in bar 73 on the fourth semiquaver from eb^1 to fb^1 and on the tenth semiquaver from f^1 to gb^1.

p. 52

Bar 74 L.H. The quaver beginning the second half of the bar, similarly as the three previous semiquavers, is recorded in the sources on the upper staff, under the R.H. part. Therefore, by taking into consideration the *all'ottava* sign, it should be read as f^2. The shape of figures in the L.H. in the previous two bars, however, testifies to the fact that Chopin was thinking of f^1 and made a mistake by transferring the L.H. part to the lower staff only in the three last semiquavers of the bar.

Bar 81 R.H. In **FE** and **EE** the melodic note d^1 in the second half of the bar is not lengthened by a dot or distinguished from the bb-d^1 third.

Bar 83 L.H. The first crotchet in **FE** is a G-d fifth. We accept the **EE** and **A**3 (→**GE**) version which stems more naturally from the previous chord. The absence of d in this version makes it possible to avoid counter-parallel fifths in relation with the successive chord. Some of the later collected editions accept the **FE** version and arbitrarily add the note d on the last quaver of bar 82.

Bar 85-86 R.H. **FE** has no tie sustaining f^1.

Bars 87-88 R.H. In **A**3 (→**GE**) there are no ties sustaining the ab^1-bb^1-f^2 chord. The repetition of this chord at the end of the phrasing slur seems to be of little probability and rather indicates that Chopin overlooked the ties.

p. 53

Bar 92 R.H. In the middle of the bar **FE** does not lengthen note d^2 with a dot and on the last quaver it has a sixth d^1-bb^1. We accept the **EE** and **A**3 (→**GE**) version (in **A**3 Chopin crossed out bb^1 and added a dot lengthening the sonority of d^2).

Bars 94-95 Some of the later collected editions arbitrarily add ties joining chords over the bar-line.

Bar 99 L.H. At the beginning of the second half of the bar **FE** and **EE** have the chord Bb-f-bb. We accept the **A**3 (→**GE**) version.

Bars 99-100 R.H. **GE** overlooks the tie sustaining d^1.

Bar 104 L.H. In the main text we give the **A**3 (→**GE**) version in which the melody in the octaves stems in the most natural way from the five-semiquaver transition in bar 103. The version given in the footnote comes from **FE** and **EE**.

Bars 108-109 and 110-111 R.H. In **A**3 (→**GE**) the sixth d^2-bb^2 in bars 108-109 is sustained by ties. In analogous bars 110-111 **A**3 discloses crossed out ties sustaining c^2-ab^2. **FE** and **EE** do not have ties in any of those passages. In the majority of the later collected editions the sixths are tied arbitrarily in both pairs of bars. The **A**3 version, with a differentiation of those passages, characteristic for Chopin, is most probably the final one.

11

p. 54 *Bar 113* R.H. The first half of the bar in **EE** sounds as follows:

and in **A3** (→**GE**):

These versions can testify to the fact that Chopin wavered in choosing the best place for interrupting the continuous progression of the sixths; they could be also the consequence of the mistakes made by Chopin and the engraver of **EE**. We accept the **FE** version since it is:
— musically the smoothest and pianistically the most convenient
— confirmed by a concurrent version of the analogous bar 115.

Bar 118 L.H. The main text comes from **FE** and **A3** (→**GE**), the variant — from **EE**. An interval on top of the progression of chords is one of the devices used by Chopin (e.g. the *Ballade in G minor*, Op. 23, bar 207), while the three-note chord alleviates somewhat the effect of the simultaneously struck doubled third g^2-g^3.

Bar 123 R.H. **A3** (→**GE**) overlooks the tie sustaining ab^1.

Bar 124 R.H. The oversights of accidentals occurring in some sources in the second half of the bar — the absence of ♮ next to c^2 in **FE** and **A3** (→**GE**) and the absence of ♮ next to f^2 in **A3** (→**GE**) — inclined the editors of the majority of the later collected editions to change those notes to cb^2 and fb^2. It should be stressed that f^2 on the last but one semiquaver does not give rise to doubts, neither as regards the sources (the flat is absent in all cases, and two sources contain naturals) nor musical (*cf.* a similar device which anticipates the major key in the *Sonata in Bb minor*, Op. 35, first movement, bar 168 and a similar juxtaposition of fb and f in adjoining octaves in this *Ballade*, bar 62, and in the *Waltz in Ab*, Op. 34 No. 1, bars 251-252), while c^2 in the ninth semiquaver is justified by tonal relations (despite the false modulations to Db minor in bars 121-124, Ab major remains the basic key from bar 115 on) and gives a smoother progression of the top semiquavers in each pair (fb^1-c^2-f^2).

p. 55 *Bars 125-126* L.H. **A3** (→**GE**) overlooks the tie sustaining bb.

Bar 127 L.H. The main text comes from **EE**, the variant — from **FE** and **A3** (→**GE**). We give priority to the **EE** version, unquestioned in this place, since we cannot exclude the possibility that the [**A1**] (→**FE**) version, copied in **A3**, is only an earlier notation, deformed by the overlooking of a tie sustaining Ab on the third eighth.

Bars 127-128 L.H. **GE** overlooks the tie linking Ab with $G♯$.

Bar 130 R.H. On the fourth semiquaver **FE** has no $g♯^1$.

Bar 134 R.H. Note a^1 on the sixth semiquaver in **FE** has the value of a semiquaver; in **EE** this sound is written as a quaver tied with an additional dotted crotchet.

Bar 136 N. B. A3 ends with this bar.

p. 56 *Bar 144* L.H. On the fifth and sixth quaver **FE**1 has no gb^1 or fb^1. In **FE**2 fb^1 is supplemented, possibly upon the basis of [**A1**]. We give the **EE** and **GE** version.

Bar 150 R.H. The main text comes from **FE** and **EE**, the variant — from **GE**. The absence of [**A3**] makes it impossible to say whether the sustaining of eb^2 is an authentic variant or an error of **GE**.

Bar 153 R.H. In the first half of the bar **FE** has the following rhythm:

Bar 154 L.H. The last semiquaver in **GE** is most probably the mistaken c^2. This sort of an error was committed at times by Chopin and particularly often by the engravers of **GE** (e.g. in bar 159, where the last semiquaver is c^2 instead of a^1).

p. 57 *Bars 156-157* R.H. **GE** has no tie sustaining ab^2.

Bars 164 and 165 R.H. Prior to the fifth semiquaver **EE** in both bars and **GE** in bar 165 add ♮. This sort of supplementation is one of the most frequent arbitrary revisions of those editions (*cf.* commentary to the *Ballade in G minor*, Op. 23, bars 45 and 47). In both cases **FE** has flats.

p. 58 *Bar 167* R.H. The main text comes from **FE** and **GE**, the variant — from **EE**.

Bar 174 R.H. At the beginning of the second half of the bar **FE** has the chord db^1-cb^2-db^2. We give the final version of **EE** and **GE**.

Bar 176 L.H. The main text comes from **FE** and **GE**, and the variant — from **EE**.

p. 59 *Bar 184* L.H. The main text comes from **GE**, and the variant — from **FE** and **EE**.

Bar 185 L.H. As the fourth and sixth semiquaver **FE** has the most probably mistaken db^1 and Bb.

p. 60 *Bar 190* L.H. The main text comes from **EE** and **GE**, and the variant — from **FE**. From the point of view of sonority the wider figuration of the **FE** version corresponds to the development of the theme as a whole (from bar 169). In **EE** and **GE** Chopin resigned from it in favour of a passage remaining within the framework designated by the directly preceding figures. *Cf.* a similarly justified variant at the end of the *Ballade in F*, Op. 38.

p. 61 *Bars 198-202* The crescendo sign and *fff* come from **FE**, where Chopin probably added them in the proofs.

Bar 200 R.H. Some of the later collected editions arbitrarily add $c♯^2$ to the first chord.

p. 62 *Bar 217* L.H. The main text comes from **EE** and **GE**. In the variant we give a pianistically slightly more difficult version of **FE**, which offers fuller harmony.

Bar 221 L.H. The **GE** version given in the footnote may be mistaken: Chopin frequently placed notes under the first line much lower, which in this case could have inclined the engraver to read F as Db.

Bars 223 and 225 R.H. Some of the later collected editions arbitrarily change f^1 to eb^1 on the first semiquaver.

Bar 226 R.H. In the last chord there is no c^2 in **FE**.

p. 63 *Bar 227* L.H. Instead of a semiquaver triplet, **EE** has a F_1-F quaver. This version, analogous to the beginning of bar 225, was probably replaced by Chopin with the **FE** and **GE** version, which does not interrupt the sequence of semiquavers and gives a logical beginning to the figures in the R.H.
L.H. In **FE** and **GE** the second semiquaver in the second half of the bar is G. This is probably an original or mistaken version of [**A1**] (→**FE**), copied owing to carelessness in [**A3**] (→**GE**). We give the **EE** version, which does not give rise to doubts and is analogous to bars 228-230.

Jan Ekier
Paweł Kamiński

Okładka i opracowanie graficzne • Cover design and graphics: MARIA EKIER
Tłumaczenie angielskie • English translation: ALEKSANDRA RODZIŃSKA-CHOJNOWSKA
Redaktor • Editor: JERZY ULMAN

Fundacja Wydania Narodowego Dzieł Fryderyka Chopina
ul. Okólnik 2, pok. 405, 00-368 Warszawa
www.chopin-nationaledition.com

Polskie Wydawnictwo Muzyczne
al. Krasińskiego 11a, 31-111 Kraków
www.pwm.com.pl

Wydanie XV • Fifteenth edition
Printed in Poland 2023

ISMN 979-0-2740-0126-1

WYDANIE NARODOWE DZIEŁ FRYDERYKA CHOPINA

Plan edycji

Seria A. UTWORY WYDANE ZA ŻYCIA CHOPINA

Seria B. UTWORY WYDANE POŚMIERTNIE

(Tytuły w nawiasach kwadratowych [] są tytułami zrekonstruowanymi przez WN, tytuły w nawiasach prostych // są dotychczas używanymi, z pewnością lub dużym prawdopodobieństwem, nieautentycznymi tytułami)

1 **A I**	**Ballady** op. 23, 38, 47, 52	
2 **A II**	**Etiudy** op. 10, 25, Trzy Etiudy (Méthode des Méthodes)	
3 **A III**	**Impromptus** op. 29, 36, 51	
4 **A IV**	**Mazurki (A)** op. 6, 7, 17, 24, 30, 33, 41, Mazurek a (Gaillard), Mazurek a (z albumu La France Musicale /Notre Temps/), op. 50, 56, 59, 63	25 **B I** **Mazurki (B)** B, G, a, C, F, G, B, As, C, a, g, f
5 **A V**	**Nokturny** op. 9, 15, 27, 32, 37, 48, 55, 62	
6 **A VI**	**Polonezy (A)** op. 26, 40, 44, 53, 61	26 **B II** **Polonezy (B)** B, g, As, gis, d, f, b, B, Ges
7 **A VII**	**Preludia** op. 28, 45	
8 **A VIII**	**Ronda** op. 1, 5, 16	
9 **A IX**	**Scherza** op. 20, 31, 39, 54	
10 **A X**	**Sonaty** op. 35, 58	
11 **A XI**	**Walce (A)** op. 18, 34, 42, 64	27 **B III** **Walce (B)** E, h, Des, As, e, Ges, As, f, a
12 **A XII**	**Dzieła różne (A)** Variations brillantes op. 12, Bolero, Tarantela, Allegro de concert, Fantazja op. 49, Berceuse, Barkarola; *suplement* – Wariacja VI z „Hexameronu"	28 **B IV** **Dzieła różne (B)** Wariacje E, Sonata c (op. 4)

29 **B V**   **Różne utwory** Marsz żałobny c, [Warianty] /Souvenir de Paganini/, Nokturn e, Ecossaises D, G, Des, Kontredans, [Allegretto], Lento con gran espressione /Nokturn cis/, Cantabile B, Presto con leggierezza /Preludium As/, Impromptu cis /Fantaisie-Impromptu/, „Wiosna" (wersja na fortepian), Sostenuto /Walc Es/, Moderato /Kartka z albumu/, Galop Marquis, Nokturn c

13 **A XIIIa**	**Koncert e-moll** op. 11 na fortepian i orkiestrę (wersja na jeden fortepian)	30 **B VIa** **Koncert e-moll** op. 11 na fortepian i orkiestrę (wersja z drugim fortepianem)
14 **A XIIIb**	**Koncert f-moll** op. 21 na fortepian i orkiestrę (wersja na jeden fortepian)	31 **B VIb** **Koncert f-moll** op. 21 na fortepian i orkiestrę (wersja z drugim fortepianem)
15 **A XIVa**	**Utwory koncertowe** na fortepian i orkiestrę op. 2, 13, 14 (wersja na jeden fortepian)	32 **B VII** **Utwory koncertowe** na fortepian i orkiestrę op. 2, 13, 14, 22 (wersja z drugim fortepianem)
16 **A XIVb**	**Polonez Es-dur** op. 22 na fortepian i orkiestrę (wersja na jeden fortepian)	
17 **A XVa**	**Wariacje na temat z** *Don Giovanniego* **Mozarta** op. 2. Partytura	
18 **A XVb**	**Koncert e-moll** op. 11. Partytura (wersja historyczna)	33 **B VIIIa** **Koncert e-moll** op. 11. Partytura (wersja koncertowa)
19 **A XVc**	**Fantazja na tematy polskie** op. 13. Partytura	
20 **A XVd**	**Krakowiak** op. 14. Partytura	
21 **A XVe**	**Koncert f-moll** op. 21. Partytura (wersja historyczna)	34 **B VIIIb** **Koncert f-moll** op. 21. Partytura (wersja koncertowa)
22 **A XVf**	**Polonez Es-dur** op. 22. Partytura	
23 **A XVI**	**Utwory na fortepian i wiolonczelę** Polonez op. 3, Grand Duo Concertant, Sonata op. 65	35 **B IX** **Rondo C-dur** na dwa fortepiany; **Wariacje D-dur** na 4 ręce; *dodatek* – wersja robocza Ronda C-dur (na jeden fortepian)
24 **A XVII**	**Trio na fortepian, skrzypce i wiolonczelę** op. 8	36 **B X** **Pieśni i piosnki**

37 **Suplement** Utwory częściowego autorstwa Chopina: Hexameron, Mazurki Fis, D, D, C, Wariacje na flet i fortepian; harmonizacje pieśni i tańców: „Mazurek Dąbrowskiego", „Boże, coś Polskę" (Largo), Bourrées G, A, Allegretto A-dur/a-moll

NATIONAL EDITION OF THE WORKS OF FRYDERYK CHOPIN

Plan of the edition

Series A. WORKS PUBLISHED DURING CHOPIN'S LIFETIME

1	**A I**	**Ballades** Opp. 23, 38, 47, 52
2	**A II**	**Etudes** Opp. 10, 25, Three Etudes (Méthode des Méthodes)
3	**A III**	**Impromptus** Opp. 29, 36, 51
4	**A IV**	**Mazurkas (A)** Opp. 6, 7, 17, 24, 30, 33, 41, Mazurka in a (Gaillard), Mazurka in a (from the album La France Musicale /Notre Temps/), Opp. 50, 56, 59, 63
5	**A V**	**Nocturnes** Opp. 9, 15, 27, 32, 37, 48, 55, 62
6	**A VI**	**Polonaises (A)** Opp. 26, 40, 44, 53, 61
7	**A VII**	**Preludes** Opp. 28, 45
8	**A VIII**	**Rondos** Opp. 1, 5, 16
9	**A IX**	**Scherzos** Opp. 20, 31, 39, 54
10	**A X**	**Sonatas** Opp. 35, 58
11	**A XI**	**Waltzes (A)** Opp. 18, 34, 42, 64
12	**A XII**	**Various Works (A)** Variations brillantes Op. 12, Bolero, Tarantella, Allegro de concert, Fantaisie Op. 49, Berceuse, Barcarolle; *supplement* – Variation VI from "Hexameron"
13	**A XIIIa**	**Concerto in E minor** Op. 11 for piano and orchestra (version for one piano)
14	**A XIIIb**	**Concerto in F minor** Op. 21 for piano and orchestra (version for one piano)
15	**A XIVa**	**Concert Works** for piano and orchestra Opp. 2, 13, 14 (version for one piano)
16	**A XIVb**	**Grande Polonaise in E♭ major** Op. 22 for piano and orchestra (version for one piano)
17	**A XVa**	**Variations on "Là ci darem" from "Don Giovanni"** Op. 2. Score
18	**A XVb**	**Concerto in E minor** Op. 11. Score (historical version)
19	**A XVc**	**Fantasia on Polish Airs** Op. 13. Score
20	**A XVd**	**Krakowiak** Op. 14. Score
21	**A XVe**	**Concerto in F minor** Op. 21. Score (historical version)
22	**A XVf**	**Grande Polonaise in E♭ major** Op. 22. Score
23	**A XVI**	**Works for Piano and Cello** Polonaise Op. 3, Grand Duo Concertant, Sonata Op. 65
24	**A XVII**	**Piano Trio** Op. 8

Series B. WORKS PUBLISHED POSTHUMOUSLY

(The titles in square brackets [] have been reconstructed by the National Edition; the titles in slant marks // are still in use today but are definitely, or very probably, not authentic)

25	**B I**	**Mazurkas (B)** in B♭, G, a, C, F, G, B♭, A♭, C, a, g, f
26	**B II**	**Polonaises (B)** in B♭, g, A♭, g♯, d, f, b♭, B♭, G♭
27	**B III**	**Waltzes (B)** in E, b, D♭, A♭, e, G♭, A♭, f, a
28	**B IV**	**Various Works (B)** Variations in E, Sonata in c (Op. 4)
29	**B V**	**Various Compositions** Funeral March in c, [Variants] /Souvenir de Paganini/, Nocturne in e, Ecossaises in D, G, D♭, Contredanse, [Allegretto],Lento con gran espressione /Nocturne in c♯/, Cantabile in B♭, Presto con leggierezza /Prelude in A♭/, Impromptu in c♯ /Fantaisie-Impromptu/, "Spring" (version for piano), Sostenuto /Waltz in E♭/, Moderato /Feuille d'Album/, Galop Marquis, Nocturne in c
30	**B VIa**	**Concerto in E minor** Op. 11 for piano and orchestra (version with second piano)
31	**B VIb**	**Concerto in F minor** Op. 21 for piano and orchestra (version with second piano)
32	**B VII**	**Concert Works** for piano and orchestra Opp. 2, 13, 14, 22 (version with second piano)
33	**B VIIIa**	**Concerto in E minor** Op. 11. Score (concert version)
34	**B VIIIb**	**Concerto in F minor** Op. 21. Score (concert version)
35	**B IX**	**Rondo in C** for two pianos; **Variations in D** for four hands; *addendum* – working version of Rondo in C (for one piano)
36	**B X**	**Songs**

37 **Supplement** Compositions partly by Chopin: Hexameron, Mazurkas in F♯, D, D, C, Variations for Flute and Piano; harmonizations of songs and dances: "The Dąbrowski Mazurka", "God who hast embraced Poland" (Largo) Bourrées in G, A, Allegretto in A major/minor